WADSWORTH
ANAEROBIC BACTERIOLOGY MANUAL

WADSWORTH ANAEROBIC BACTERIOLOGY MANUAL

Fourth Edition

VERA L. SUTTER, Ph.D.
DIANE M. CITRON, B.S.
MARTHA A.C. EDELSTEIN, B.A.
SYDNEY M. FINEGOLD, M.D.

Veterans Administration Wadsworth Medical Center,
and Departments of Medicine, and Microbiology and Immunology,
UCLA School of Medicine, Los Angeles, California

PUBLISHING COMPANY

PUBLISHING COMPANY
P.O. Box 68
Belmont, California 94002
(415) 591-3505

Sutter, Vera L., Ph.D., 1924
Citron, Diane M., B.S., 1943
Edelstein, Martha A.C., B.A., 1949
Finegold, Sydney M., M.D., 1921

Managing editor: Stuart Hoffman
Cover design: Douglas Hurd
Graphics: Cheryl Baca
Color separations: Production Resource
Consulting Editor: Susan G. Kelley, Ph.D.
Photography: Martin Cohen

FOURTH EDITION

Previous editions published in 1972 and 1975 by the
Department of Continuing Education in Health Sciences,
University Extension, and the School of Medicine, UCLA;
third edition published by C.V. Mosby Co.

Printed in the United States of America

Paperback: ISBN:0-89863-098-3
Hardback: ISBN:0-89863-100-9

PREFACE

It has become clear in recent years that anaerobic bacteria are important causes of many different types of infection. Any type of bacterial infection in humans may involve anaerobes.

Anaerobic infections are beyond question the most frequently overlooked of all bacterial infections. The opportunity for overlooking anaerobes is greatest when they are present in mixed culture, as they commonly are. Isolation of an accompanying facultative organism, particularly if it has the same general characteristics on Gram stain (that is to say, both gram-negative bacilli), may lull the unaware bacteriologist into a false sense of security. When no aerobes or facultative organisms are present on culture and Gram stain has revealed bacteria, it is considerably easier to suspect and to isolate the anaerobes. The large number of reports of anaerobes (mostly gram-negative bacilli and especially the *Bacteroides fragilis* group) in bacteremia reflects the ease of recovery of these organisms in pure culture.

Failure to recognize the importance of anaerobic bacteria in infection in the past must be blamed on both clinicians and microbiologists. Fortunately, as one group becomes more aware of the role of these organisms, the other also does. However, there is still a need for education of both groups as to the importance of these organisms and optimum procedures for their recovery and identification. A monograph designed primarily for the clinician (46) provides a detailed review of the clinical aspects of anaerobic infection.

This manual is aimed chiefly at the laboratory worker. It is our intent to emphasize practical aspects of anaerobic bacteriology for clinical laboratories. Although certain fastidious anaerobes require very specialized anaerobic techniques (the anaerobic chamber or glove-box procedure and the roll-tube or prereduced medium procedures), such delicate organisms have seldom been involved in true infection.

While we emphasize the simpler, more rapid techniques suitable for processing clinical specimens in small laboratories, we also present descriptions of the two more rigorous techniques, because they can be useful in clinical laboratories that process large numbers of specimens for anaerobic culture and because they are essential for normal flora studies.

This manual concerns only organisms encountered in humans. Animal strains may have different growth requirements and frequently have different antimicrobial susceptibility patterns.

We would like to express our appreciation to the many people who kindly offered suggestions for improvements since the first edition of our manual was published in 1972. Included are Maria Appleman, Howard Attebery, Kenneth Bricknell, Walker Carter, Ron Gee, Shushan Halebian, Betty Harris, Lubna

Kureschi, Richard Kwok, Cynnthia Miranda-Reichelderfer, Pete Rose, Paul Sugihara, Nadine Sullivan, Joe Trammell, Valerie Vargo, Kevin Ward, Hannah Wexler, Palma Wideman, Brenda Wield, and Sally Young.

We appreciate the excellent help with illustrations from Marty Cohen, Pete Rose and the Medical Media Service of the VA Wadsworth Medical Center.

We are indebted to Mrs. Kimi Ishii for excellent suggestions for the arrangement of material and for typing the manuscript.

Vera L. Sutter
Diane M. Citron
Martha A.C. Edelstein
Sydney M. Finegold

CONTENTS

FIGURES

COLOR PLATES

CHAPTER 1

GENERAL CONSIDERATIONS

Since many anaerobes grow more slowly than facultative or aerobic bacteria and since clinical specimens yielding anaerobic bacteria not uncommonly contain several organisms, considerable time may elapse before the laboratory is able to provide a final report. Indeed, at times it may literally take weeks before certain specimens with a complex flora are worked up definitively. The question then arises as to whether the bacteriologic data are really beneficial to the clinician. Aside from the time factor, how much data are useful to the clinician? Is the clinician interested in accurate species and subspecies identification or will general identification, with susceptibility data, suffice to permit effective treatment of the patient? Even when the clinician is interested in detailed, accurate bacteriologic data — if only for academic reasons — does cost-benefit analysis warrant providing them? Just how far should the laboratory go in processing anaerobic cultures? These are difficult questions, and the answers vary according to specific circumstances; hard and fast rules cannot be set up.

Clearly, it is important that the laboratory provide as much information as possible as soon as it can after receipt of the specimen. This is particularly true, of course, in the case of very ill patients. It is the physician's responsibility to call such patients to the attention of the microbiologist. A series of reports on each individual specimen would provide the clinician with information in optimal fashion. The initial report, at least in the case of very sick patients, should be an interpretation of the Gram stain and any other direct examination of the specimen. The microbiologist must not hesitate to express judgment on likely possibilities, not only from direct examination, but (later) from observation of colonial characteristics. This presumes, of course, that the microbiologist is well informed and applies rational judgment. After 18 to 24 hours, examination of aerobic cultures (and certain special anaerobic cultures) permits the microbiologist to provide a more reliable report. Similarly, examination of routine anaerobic cultures after 48 hours provides even further information, especially when selective media are used. A number of rapid diagnostic procedures may be employed to expedite presumptive or definitive identification.

Certain anaerobes should be identified, at least presumptively, as rapidly as possible. Two outstanding examples are the *Bacteroides fragilis* group and *Clos-*

tridium perfringens, the former because it is the most commonly encountered and most resistant to antimicrobial agents and the latter because it may produce devastating disease. Fortunately, these organisms grow rapidly and with little difficulty. Means are available for readily recovering them from mixed cultures, and they can be identified quite simply and rapidly.

Any laboratory engaged in anaerobic cultivation should be able to recover in pure culture all anaerobes present in clinical specimens, to maintain them in a viable state, and to do at least preliminary characterization. This, with identification of certain key organisms such as *B. fragilis* and *C. perfringens*, provides the clinician with the data needed to successfully manage patients with anaerobic infections. The above two anaerobes, along with the pigmented *Bacteroides*, *Fusobacterium nucleatum*, and the anaerobic cocci (these three groups are also readily identified) account for approximately two-thirds of all clinically significant infections involving anaerobes. Broth disk susceptibility tests are easy to perform and should be available in most laboratories.

Although we recognize that a number of smaller laboratories may find it difficult to go beyond what has been outlined in the preceding two paragraphs and that cost may be a problem, we nonetheless urge full, definitive identification whenever possible. As an example, speciation within the *B. fragilis* group may provide useful information. *B. fragilis* and *B. thetaiotaomicron* are commonly found as pathogens; recovery of *B. ovatus* might mean contamination of a specimen with normal bowel flora. Similarly, speciation within the *B. ureolyticus* group is important. *B. gracilis* is much more pathogenic than *B. ureolyticus* and is much more resistant to antimicrobial agents. If an organism initially felt to be *B. fragilis* from a patient with bacteremia of unknown source was subsequently identified as *B. splanchnicus*, this would indicate the bowel as the likely source; whereas, if it were *B. fragilis,* the portal of entry might also have been the female genital tract or elsewhere. Identification of a *Clostridium* isolated from the blood as *C. septicum* provides the clinician with a valuable clue, as there is a strong association between bacteremia with this organism and malignancy or other disease of the colon, especially the cecum. Exact identification of an organism isolated from a patient with two or more episodes of infection helps distinguish between recurrence (which may imply tumor, foreign body, or an undrained abscess) and a new infection.

Short cuts to identification, if not applied intelligently, may lead to significant errors in the case of anaerobes, since these organisms are often pleomorphic (rods being mistaken for cocci and *vice versa*), and do not always show spores readily, while gram-positive forms destain readily. We realize, of course, that the use of limited identification procedures is necessary in most clinical laboratories. However, careful application of knowledge of the significance of various organisms in specific situations and thoughtful use of limited approaches keep costs within reason and keep the laboratory's workload manageable without compromising patient care.

Quantitation of results is of particular importance in anaerobic bacteriology since anaerobic infections are frequently mixed and the relative importance of various organisms in complex mixtures may often be deduced from this type of information. Formal quantitation is not usually necessary; designation as "heavy growth", "few colonies", and so on, is adequate.

Accurate bacteriologic data permit one to define the role of various anaerobes in different infectious processes and the prognosis associated with these. Definitive identification is important in educating clinicians as to the role of various organisms in infectious processes and prevents deterioration of the skills and interest of the bacteriologist.

ANAEROBES AS NORMAL FLORA

A knowledge of the presence of specific anaerobes as normal flora at various sites in the body is important in several ways. Since most anaerobic infections arise in proximity to mucosal surfaces, where anaerobes predominate as normal flora, information on which organisms make up the indigenous flora at these sites enables one to anticipate the presence of certain organisms in particular specimens and thus to assist the clinician in choosing the proper drugs for initiating therapy. This information also helps the microbiologist to choose selective and other media that might be particularly useful. Knowledge of the normal flora of various regions may also allow one to judge more readily whether a given isolate is significant. For example, *Propionibacterium* in a single blood culture most often represents "contamination" from the patient's skin, particularly if growth does not appear until after several days. Conversely, the presence of a particular organism in blood cultures may suggest the portal of entry for the bacteremia.

Table 1-1 indicates the incidence of certain anaerobes as normal flora at various sites in humans. Additional data on anaerobes as indigenous flora are found in Rosebury's classic book (133) and in references 16, 48, 156.

CLINICAL BACKGROUND

Incidence of anaerobes in infection

Anaerobes may cause any type of infection in humans. In a number of infections, anaerobic bacteria are the predominant pathogens or are commonly found; these are listed in Table 1-2. When information regarding incidence of anaerobes in these infections is available, it has been indicated. It must be emphasized, however, that the majority of published studies on anaerobic infections has been retrospective. The bacteriologic methods, particularly the anaerobic methods, were not uniform and, in many instances, not optimal. Therefore, some of these incidence figures are undoubtedly low. Several articles emphasizing various aspects of anaerobic infections are also indicated in the table and are recommended for those wishing to read further on this subject.

Other studies not included in Table 1-2 incorporate inaccuracies related to uncertainty about the clinical significance of isolates and to selection of certain types of specimens that would certainly contain elements of the normal flora. In this type of study, of course, the incidence of anaerobes may be falsely high.

Table 1-1 Incidence of various anaerobes as normal flora in humans

| | | Non-spore-forming bacilli | | | | | | | Cocci | |
| | | Gram-positive | | | | | Gram-negative | | | |
	Clostridium	Actinomyces	Bifidobacterium	Eubacterium	Lactobacillus†	Propionibacterium	Bacteroides	Fusobacterium	Gram-positive	Gram-negative
Skin	0	0	0	±	0	2	0	0	1	0
Upper respiratory tract*	0	1	0	±	0	1	1	1	1	1
Mouth	±	1	1	1	1	±	2	2	2	2
Intestine	2	±	2	2	1-2	±	2	±	2	±
External genitalia	0	0	0	U	0	U	1	1	1	0
Urethra	±	0	0	U	±	0	1	1	±	U
Vagina	±	0	±	±	2	1	1	±	2	1

Key
U, unknown; O, not found or rare; ±, irregular; 1, usually present; 2, usually present in large numbers

* Includes nasal passages, nasopharynx, oropharynx, and tonsils
† Includes anaerobic, microaerophilic, and facultative strains

Table 1-3 details our own experience with recovery of anaerobes from clinical specimens.

Clues to anaerobic infection

Certain hints suggest to the microbiologist that a given specimen is likely to contain anaerobic bacteria:

1. Foul odor to specimen
2. Location of infection in proximity to a mucosal surface
3. Infections secondary to human or animal bite
4. Gas in specimen
5. Previous therapy with aminoglycoside antibiotics (such as gentamicin or amikacin) in the absence of concomitant effective coverage vs. anaerobes
6. Black discoloration of blood-containing exudates; these exudates may fluoresce red under ultraviolet light (infections involving pigmented *Bacteroides*)
7. Presence of "sulfur granules" in discharges (actinomycosis)
8. Unique morphology on Gram stain
9. Failure of organisms seen on Gram stain of original exudate to grow aerobically
10. Growth in anaerobic zone of fluid media or of agar deeps
11. Anaerobic growth on media containing 75 to 100 μg/ml of kanamycin, neomycin, or paromomycin (or medium also containing 7.5 μg/ml of vancomycin, in the case of gram-negative anaerobic bacilli) or on other selective media such as BBE, CCFA and RIF (see Appendix)
12. Characteristic colonies on anaerobic agar plates (for example, *F. nucleatum* and *C. perfringens*)
13. Young colonies of pigmented *Bacteroides* (growth from anaerobic blood agar plate) may fluoresce red under ultraviolet light

Table 1-2 Infections commonly involving anaerobes

	Incidence %	Proportion of cultures positive for anaerobes yielding only anaerobes	Reference
Bacteremia	20	4/5	45,172
Bacteremia secondary to tooth extraction	84	21/25	33
Ocular infections	38	10/43	82
Corneal ulcers	7	9/11	125
Central nervous system			
Brain abscess	89	1/2-2/3	68
Extra or subdural empyema	10		161
Head and neck			
Chronic sinusitis	52	4/5*	52
Acute sinusitis	7		64
Chronic otitis media	56	1/10	23
	59	11/115	7
	33	0	81
Cholesteatoma	92	1/11	77
Neck space infections	100	3/4	11
Wound infection following head and neck surgery	95	0	19
Peritonsillar abscess	76	6/28	50
Dental, oral, facial			
Bite wounds	47	1/34	55
Dental and oral			97
Orofacial, of dental origin	94	4/10	31
Root canal infection	95	13/18	155
	100	18/55	57
Periodontal abscess	100	0/9	120
Dental abscess, endodontic origin	100	8/12	22
	90	6/9	182
Thoracic			
Aspiration pneumonia	93	1/2†	12
	62	1/3	99
	100	1/3	56
Lung abscess	93	1/2-2/3	13
	85	3/4	20
Bronchiectasis	76	1/3	14
Empyema (nonsurgical)	62	1/2	20

* Twenty-three of 28 cultures (82%) yielding heavy growth of one or more organisms had only anaerobes present

† Aspiration pneumonia occurring in the community rather than in the hospital involves anaerobes to the exclusion of aerobic or faculative forms two-thirds of the time.

Table 1-2 Infections commonly involving anaerobes (cont.)

	Incidence %	Proportion of cultures positive for anaerobes yielding only anaerobes	Reference
Abdominal			
Intra-abdominal infection	86	1/10	51
(general)	90	1/3	111
	81	1/3	163
	94	1/7	58
Appendicitis with peritonitis	96	1/100	2
Liver abscess	52	1/3	136
Other intra-abdominal infection (postsurgery)	93	1/6	61
Wound infection following bowel surgery			46
Biliary tract	45	0	141
	41	2/117	41
Obstetric-gynecologic			
Miscellaneous types	100	1/3	167
	74	1/3	164
	72		92
Pelvic abscess	88	1/2	1
Vulvovaginal abscess	75	1/4	123
Vaginal cuff abscess	98	1/30	63
Septic abortion, sepsis	67		135
	63		145
Pelvic inflammatory disease	25	1/14	30
	48	1/7	43
Soft tissue and miscellaneous			
Nonclostridial crepitant cellulitis	75	1/12	102
Pilonidal sinus	73 +		124
Bite wound infection	(see Dental, oral, facial)		
Diabetic foot ulcers	95	1/20	100
Infected diabetic gangrene (deep tissue culture)	85	1/11	138
Soft tissue abscesses	60	1/4	76
Cutaneous abscesses	62	1/5	108
Decubitus ulcers with bacteremia	63		29
Osteomyelitis	40	1/10	95
Gas gangrene (clostridial myonecrosis)			3
Breast abscess			46
Perirectal abscess			46

Table 1.3 Incidence of specific anaerobes in various infections (Wadsworth VA Medical Center experience 1973-1983)

Specimen source or type of infection	Number of positive specimens surveyed	Total isolates	Average no. of anaerobes per specimen	B. fragilis	B. thetatiotaomicron	Other bile-resistant Bacteroides †	B. melaninogenicus-loescheii-denticola	B. intermedius-corporis grp.	B. asaccharolyticus	Other pigmented Bacteroides sp.	B. ureolyticus group	Other bile-sensitive Bacteroides sp. +	Other Bacteroides §	F. nucleatum	F. necrophorum
Blood	175	226	1.3	33*	9	13	1	0	1	0	1	3	5	2	7
Central nervous system	19	32	1.6	0	0	0	0	5	5	0	5	5	11	32	5
Head and neck infections	75	349	4.6	0	1	3	40	49	5	12	7	72	41	40	1
Dental	9	35	3.9	0	0	0	11	11	0	0	0	22	11	0	22
Human bites	25	72	2.9	0	0	0	20	48	0	0	4	48	20	28	0
Animal bites	33	81	2.5	3	0	0	6	6	6	3	0	12	24	15	0
TTA** & pleural fluid	196	656	3.3	4	1	2	23	30	3	6	9	47	33	29	3
Miscellaneous soft tissue infections above the waist	79	203	2.6	5	0	0	4	18	10	3	9	29	42	22	4
Intraabdominal infections	185	763	4.1	54	30	50	5	12	6	5	5	15	24	13	4
Perirectal abscess	34	158	4.6	68	32	62	6	6	26	12	12	29	21	9	0
Decubitus ulcers	54	212	3.9	50	26	48	4	6	17	9	2	11	35	2	0
Foot ulcers	222	645	2.9	30	6	12	5	8	10	7	5	14	20	4	1
Miscellaneous soft tissue infections below the waist	135	375	2.7	35	15	14	4	5	9	5	6	9	14	5	0
Osteomyelitis	49	139	2.8	12	6	4	6	2	2	10	8	12	24	6	2

*   Numbers in this table represent numbers of isolates per 100 specimens containing anaerobes.

†   B. distasonis, B. vulgatus, B. ovatus, B. uniformis, B. splanchnicus, B. eggerthii, and "B. fragilis group — no good fit".

+   B. oris, B. buccae, B. oralis, B. bivius,. B. disiens, B. buccalis, B. veroralis.

Table 1.3 Incidence of specific anaerobes in various infections (cont.)

Specimen source or type of infection	F. mortiferum-varium grp.	Other Fusobacterium π	Other Gram-negative bacilli	Peptostreptococcus sp. #	Veillonella	Acidaminococcus, Megasphaera, unidentified GNC	Clostridium perfringens	Other Clostridium sp.	Actinomyces sp.	Bifidobacterium sp.	Lactobacillus sp.	P. acnes	Other Propionibacterium sp.	Eubacterium sp.
Blood	1	1	1	7	1	1	5	21	0	1	1	3	0	7
Central nervous system	0	0	0	21	5	0	0	0	32	0	0	37	0	0
Head and neck infections	0	5	1	85	33	4	0	0	8	3	17	7	3	25
Dental	0	11	0	178	33	0	0	0	44	0	22	0	11	11
Human bites	0	0	0	48	40	0	0	4	12	0	4	4	4	4
Animal bites	0	39	3	21	9	0	3	0	21	0	0	33	21	18
TTA** & pleural fluid	0	10	3	33	26	1	5	5	14	5	15	4	2	23
Miscellaneous soft tissue infections above the waist	0	4	1	62	11	0	4	1	6	0	6	4	5	11
Intraabdominal infections	4	5	0	51	7	2	15	44	3	2	12	6	1	37
Perirectal abscess	3	3	3	68	12	6	6	59	0	0	3	3	0	18
Decubitus ulcers	2	2	0	107	7	0	6	39	9	0	6	4	0	13
Foot ulcers	1	3	1	111	5	0	2	7	6	0	5	5	2	12
Miscellaneous soft tissue infections below the waist	1	2	1	98	7	1	5	6	9	1	3	4	2	16
Osteomyelitis	0	0	0	133	2	0	0	2	10	4	2	16	0	16

§   Includes non-speciable Bacteroides.
π   Includes non-speciable Fusobacterium.
Includes strains formerly identified as Peptococcus.
**   Transtracheal aspirates.

CHAPTER **2**

SPECIMENS AND CULTURE TECHNIQUES

SPECIMEN COLLECTION

Since anaerobes may cause or contribute to infections of all types, it is clear that all specimens free of contamination with normal flora should be cultured anaerobically. The following specimens may be contaminated with normal flora and ordinarily should not be cultured anaerobically:

Throat swabs

Nasopharyngeal swabs

Gingival swabs

Expectorated sputum

Sputum obtained by nasotracheal or orotracheal suction

Specimens obtained via a bronchoscope

Gastric contents
Small bowel contents } except in "blind loop" and similar syndromes

Large bowel contents (except for *C. difficile*, *C. botulinum*)

Ileostomy, colostomy effluents

Feces (except for *C. difficile*, *C. botulinum*)

Voided urine, catheterized urine

Vaginal swabs, cervical swabs (see discussion of endometritis)

Proper collection (that is, taking care to avoid inclusion of normal flora), cannot be overemphasized, because indigenous anaerobes are often present in such large numbers that even minimal contamination of a specimen with normal flora can give very misleading results and cause much wasted effort. Collection methods that avoid contamination with normal flora are listed in Table 2-1.

Coughed sputum is unsuitable, because it becomes contaminated with normal flora anaerobes on its passage through the mouth and pharynx. For the same reason, bronchoscopic specimens[*] or those obtained by nasotracheal tube suctioning also should not be cultured anaerobically. The sampling tube always

---

[*] Preliminary studies (183) indicate that with use of a telescoping double catheter plugged at the distal end with polyethylene glycol (Medi-Tech)® to protect a bronchial brush and with quantitation, it may be possible to get reliable cultures (including anaerobic cultures) via a bronchoscope. This remains to be established.

Table 2-1 Recommended specimen collection methods for anaerobic culture

Source	Procedure
Pulmonary	Percutaneous transtracheal aspiration or direct lung puncture; (Medi-Tech® plugged double lumen catheter and bronchial brush for bronchoscopic specimens not fully established as valid)
Pleural	Thoracentesis
Urinary tract	Suprapubic percutaneous bladder aspiration, nephrostomy specimens
Abscesses	Needle and syringe aspiration of closed abscess; use of swabs much less desirable
Female genital tract	Use culdocentesis to obtain specimens, when possible, after decontaminating the vagina with povidone-iodine; Medi-Tech® double catheter and bronchial brush or sterile swab for uterine cavity specimens (not suitable for postpartum endometritis). See note above under Pulmonary.
Sinus tracts or draining wounds	Aspiration by syringe and small plastic catheter introduced as deeply as possible through decontaminated skin orifice; specimen obtained at surgery from depths of wound or underlying bone lesion always preferable; curettings and tissue biopsies provide excellent material

contacts normal flora on its downward path. Adequate pleuropulmonary specimens for anaerobic culture can be obtained by transtracheal aspiration (TTA), thoracentesis or direct percutaneous needle puncture and aspiration of lung infiltrates or abscesses. Tracheostomy tube specimens may provide useful material when this device is first inserted; when it has been in place for awhile there is inevitable contamination with oropharyngeal secretions, whether or not there is an inflated cuff.

Voided urine specimens are unsuitable for anaerobic culture because the distal portion of the urethra and the meatus are colonized with a normal flora containing anaerobes, which will contaminate urine passing through these areas. If a suprapubic bladder catheter or cystostomy or nephrostomy tube is in place, reliable urine specimens may be collected from these sites.

Endometritis presents a very difficult problem. Anaerobes are clearly very important in this infection which involves various elements of the cervical and vaginal flora. However, most cases of endometritis follow childbirth, and it has been demonstrated that in the postpartum period, *whether or not there is endometrial infection*, significant numbers of anaerobes and other organisms from the cervical and vaginal flora are found in the uterine cavity. There are not even quantitative differences between infected and uninfected patients. This situation may apply also in postabortal endometritis. Thus, one should obtain blood cultures and culture any better sources of material that may be available. Culture for the *B. fragilis* group may be useful. Since the presence of the *B. fragilis* group in this type of specimen may indicate a poorer prognosis and since this organism is so much more resistant to antimicrobials than other anaerobes, it makes sense to determine whether or not it is present. This can be done readily with an excellent selective and differential medium, Bacteroides bile esculin agar.

Infections of decubitus ulcers commonly involve anaerobic organisms, particularly when the decubitus is in the vicinity of the anus (sacral decubiti and decubiti of the hips and buttocks). Since these areas are subject to fecal contamination (and this is typically how they become infected), it is clear that the area must be thoroughly cleansed with an appropriate antiseptic agent before cultures are taken. Whenever possible, of course, one should aspirate collections of pus from under skin flaps or from deep pockets using a syringe and needle. The same considerations apply to other lesions in these areas (perirectal abscess, for example).

Specimens that are normally sterile (such as spinal fluid and blood and joint fluid) may be collected in the usual fashion after thorough skin decontamination.

In general, material for anaerobic culture is best obtained using a needle and syringe. All air must be expelled from the syringe and needle. Use of swabs is a poor alternative for a number of reasons, including excessive exposure of the specimen to the deleterious effects of oxygen and drying. The overlying and adjacent areas must be prepared carefully with an antiseptic agent to eliminate surface organisms before cultures are obtained.

Laboratory personnel should reject specimens not obtained in a proper manner and should be supported in this position by infectious disease clinicians and/or pathologists. In rejecting specimens, of course, the reasons should be explained to the requesting physician. Specimens should never be discarded before discussion with the requesting clinician. Some specimens, such as those taken at the time of surgery, are difficult or impossible to replace. Those specimens that cannot be replaced should be Gram-stained and interpreted as carefully as possible.

SPECIMEN TRANSPORT

Another crucial factor affecting the ultimate success of anaerobic cultures is the transport of specimens. The bacteria must be protected from the lethal effects of oxygen during the period from time of collection of the specimen until it is set up anaerobically in the laboratory. Immediately following collection, specimens should be placed into an anaerobic transporter such as the Hungate tube pictured in Fig. 2-1. The tube contains oxygen-free gas and an agar or broth indicator system; it is sealed by a screw cap with a butyl rubber diaphragm. The material should remain in this anaerobic environment until just prior to media inoculation, when it is removed with a needle and syringe. Similar versions of this tube are available commercially (Anaport vials, Scott Laboratories; Port-a-Cul, Baltimore Biological Laboratories [BBL], and others) (Fig. 2-2). The syringe and needle assembly used for obtaining the specimen may be used for transport directly if it is taken immediately to the laboratory (Fig. 2-3). This method should be used only when the specimen can be processed within 30 minutes. If a specimen can only be collected using a swab, one should obtain swabs that have been maintained in an anaerobic tube and that can be placed into a second (anaerobic transport) tube containing a column of prereduced and anaerobically sterilized (PRAS) semisolid Cary and Blair medium. The PRAS Cary and Blair agar is available commercially (BBL), although no anaerobic swab is provided. Anaerobic swabs and PRAS Cary and Blair medium are available from Anaerobe Systems. Another commercially available transport system is the Vacutainer™ Anaerobic Transporter (Becton-Dickinson [B-D]), which has a self-contained reducing mechanism to reduce oxygen introduced with the swab (Fig. 2-4).

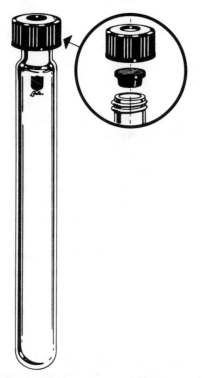

Fig. 2-1. (above) Diagram of disposable Hungate tube, illustrating component parts: tube, diaphragm and screwcap. (Courtesy, Bellco Glass Inc.)

Fig. 2-2. (below) Anaerobic transporter. These are available from several sources or may be prepared as directed in the Appendix using Hungate tubes.

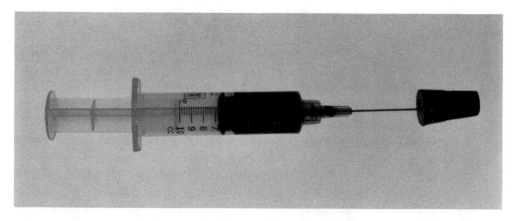

Fig 2-3. Specimens that can be processed within 30 minutes may be transported in the syringe in which the specimen was collected. All air should be expelled from the syringe and needle and the needle sealed with a sterile rubber stopper.

For transporting tissue, the Bio-Bag is most suitable; it may also be used for fluid specimens and swabs. The tissue or other material is placed into a sterile plastic tube, syringe, or glass vial with the cap screwed on loosely, and is then placed inside the bag. The top of the bag is sealed with a heat sealer, or rolled down several times and taped securely with any good tape with good adhesive quality. The indicator and gas generator are then activated according to the manufacturer's instructions.

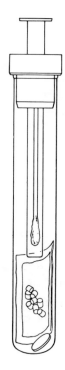

Fig 2-4. Vacutainer™ Anaerobic Transporter (B-D). The cotton swab is attached to a plunger in the stopper. The stopper and swab are removed, and the specimen can be collected on the swab, or tissue or fluid can be placed in the inner tube. The stopper is replaced and the plunger pushed down to release the central tube with the specimen into the outer tube and close the hole in the rubber stopper. The outer tube contains a mixture of H_2, CO_2, and N_2 and palladium covered catalyst pellet. The hydrogen combines with the oxygen introduced with the specimen (forming water) to achieve anaerobiosis.

ANAEROBIC CULTURE TECHNIQUES

Anaerobic methods include the use of anaerobic jars, Bio-Bags®, the PRAS method of Hungate (75) (and modifications), and the anaerobic chamber or glove box. The last two techniques are rather time consuming, require complex and expensive equipment, and utilize PRAS media. They are essential for work on anaerobes of the normal flora. Two comparative studies have shown that when clinical specimens are collected, transported, and processed properly, recovery of clinically significant anaerobes is as good with anaerobic jars as with the more complex methods (86,134).

Large anaerobic incubators that have been available should not be used for routine work because of the excessive exposure of cultures to oxygen that is inherent in their use. The same criticism applies to the large diameter GasPak-150 jar when used for primary isolation. Incubators inside anaerobic chambers do work well, especially if plates are kept in plastic bags (loosely taped) to maintain moisture content.

Use of liquid media as the only anaerobic culture technique is not satisfactory except in the case of blood cultures. Anaerobic infections are frequently mixed, and it would be impossible to isolate the individual components of the mixture from liquid media. Facultative organisms may grow better than anaerobes, making isolation of the latter difficult or impossible. Quantitation is not possible. Liquid media, therefore, should be used only as an adjunct to other anaerobic culture methods.

Blood culture techniques

Liquid media. There are a number of commercially available media that appear to be satisfactory for recovery of anaerobic bacteria (172). Some contain sodium polyanethol sulfonate (SPS), which has been reported to enhance the recovery of anaerobes but may be inhibitory to *Peptostreptococcus anaerobius*. This inhibitory effect can be overcome by addition of 1.2% gelatin. Some of the media available in unvented bottles containing 100 ml of medium, with or without SPS, and prepared under vacuum with CO_2 added are tryptic soy broth (Difco), thiol broth (Difco), Columbia broth (Difco), trypticase soy broth (B-D), and thioglycollate medium 135C (BD) (When referring to the specific product, thioglycollate medium-135C, the word thioglycollate will contain two ls. When referring to thioglycolate generically, the word thioglycolate will contain one l).

PRAS-supplemented brain-heart infusion yeast extract broth (Scott Laboratories), supplemented peptone broth (B-D), and a radiometric method (BACTEC®) are also available. Data thus far available do not indicate any superiority of these systems over unvented media under vacuum with CO_2.

After properly cleaning and disinfecting the skin, draw blood from the patient and inoculate it *immediately* into the medium at a ratio of 1 ml of blood to 10 to 20 ml of medium. It is advisable to inoculate two bottles, venting one for maximal recovery of strict aerobes (these should also be checked for anaerobes) and leaving the other unvented for recovery of anaerobes.

Cultures should be examined daily for turbidity, colonies, hemolysis, or gas. Gram-stained smears and "blind" aerobic subcultures should be made routinely after the first 6 to 12 hours of incubation, and anaerobic subcultures should be made on all bottles showing macroscopic growth (117, 122). Negative culture plates should be held for 7 days and thioglycolate medium for 2 weeks. The thioglycolate medium should be subcultured after one week if plates are negative.

Solid media. After proper decontamination of the skin and the collection tube, blood may be drawn into a Vacutainer tube containing SPS and transported to the laboratory for the preparation of pour plates. Blood is mixed in tubes of melted and cooled medium such as Brucella agar (1 ml to each of 5 to 10 tubes containing 19 ml of agar). The contents of the tubes are poured into Petri dishes, allowed to solidify, and then are incubated anaerobically, under 10% CO_2, and in air. Although this method has the advantage of providing quantitation and isolation, it is more cumbersome.

Jar techniques

A number of acceptable jars are available currently. They are used primarily with plated media. The introduction of a gas mixture containing H_2 into a jar is followed by catalytic conversion of the oxygen in the jar with hydrogen to water, thus establishing anaerobiosis. A catalyst composed of palladium-coated alumina pellets (Coy Manufacturing Co. and Engelhard Industries) held in a wire mesh is preferred, since there is no explosion hazard with this "cold" catalyst, and it is more convenient to use. However, the pellets can be inactivated by excess moisture and H_2S. Therefore, they should be reactivated *after each use* by heating the basket or sachet of pellets to 160°C in a drying oven for 1-1/2 to 2 hours. It is convenient to have a few extra baskets or sachets of catalysts for this purpose. Reactivated catalysts should be stored in a dry area until used. We do not recommend the use of jars without catalysts.

Anaerobic jars can be set up by two different methods. The easiest utilizes a commercially available H_2 and CO_2 generator envelope, activated simply by adding 10 ml of water (Fig. 2-5). The envelope is placed in the jar with the inoculated plates, water is added, and the jar is sealed. Production of heat within a few minutes (detected by touching the top of the jar) and subsequent development of moisture on the walls of the jar are indications that the catalyst and generator envelope are functioning properly. Reduced conditions are achieved in 1 to 2 hours, although the methylene blue or resazurin indicators take longer to decolorize. Alternatively, the "evacuation-replacement" system may be used. Air is removed from the sealed jar by drawing a vacuum of 25 inches of Hg. This process is repeated two times, filling the jar with an oxygen-free gas such as N_2 between evacuations. The final fill of the jar is made with a gas mixture containing 80% to 90% N_2, 5% to 10% H_2, and 5% to 10% CO_2. Carbon dioxide is included since many anaerobes require it for maximal growth. The atmosphere in the jars should be monitored by including an indicator to check anaerobiosis. Anaerobiosis is achieved more quickly by the "evacuation-

a

b

c

Fig. 2-5.   Anaerobic jars. a. Gas-Pak® (photo courtesy Baltimore Biological Laboratories). b. Oxoid® c. Scott® photo courtesy Scott Laboratories, Inc.)

replacement'' method. Both methods give comparable yields of anaerobes from clinical specimens if the specimen is properly transported and set up in jars immediately after plates are streaked.

Bio-Bag® Technique

The Bio-Bag® (Marion Scientific Corp.) consists of a clear, gas-impermeable bag, an ampule containing resazurin indicator, and a gas generator ampule. One or two plates are placed inside the bag (Bio-Bag type A®), and it is sealed with a heat sealer (Fig. 2-6). The indicator ampule is crushed; the gas generator is then activated. Reduced conditions are achieved within one-half hour. Organisms grow and maintain viability for up to one week. These bags are especially convenient for incubating primary plates or in other circumstances where few plates are used.

Prereduced anaerobically sterilized (PRAS) and roll-tube techniques

PRAS tubes are made by combining the constituents of the media, boiling the liquid to remove dissolved air, and then gassing-out with an oxygen-free gas. During the remainder of the media-making process (sterilization, inoculation, and subculture), air is prevented from gaining entrance into the containers by a gassing procedure or by keeping the container stoppered or sealed. To lower the E_h of the media, a reducing agent is added before sterilization. Details of PRAS media preparation and inoculation are given in the VPI *Anaerobe Laboratory Manual* (69). PRAS media are available from commercial sources (Carr-Scarborough Microbiologicals, Inc. and Scott Laboratories, Inc.).

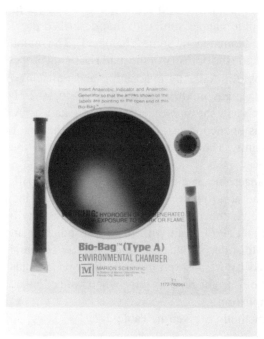

Fig 2-6. Bio-Bag™ containing a *Bacteroides* bile esculin agar plate inoculated with *B. fragilis*.

PRAS tubes can be inoculated by either the closed or open methods. In the closed method, also known as the Hungate method, a syringe and needle are used to inoculate through the rubber seal. Hungate gives a complete description of this process (75). Biochemical testing for speciation may be done by this technique; the PRAS II® system (Scott Laboratories, Inc.) is excellent for this purpose.

PRAS tubes can also be inoculated by the open method which consists of removing the rubber stopper and inserting a cannula that has oxygen-free gas flowing from the tip. While the tube is open, inoculation can be accomplished by loop or Pasteur pipet. Special equipment can be purchased for the inoculating procedure (Bellco Glass, Inc. and Kontes), or a simple inoculating device — using a bent needle attached to tubing and connected to a ring stand — can be made. The PRAS tube is held by an adjustable laboratory clamp containing an aluminum test tube cap within which the tube is placed. Since some batches of tungsten wire may oxidize PRAS media, it is advisable to use platinum wires and loops for PRAS techniques.

Anaerobic chamber techniques

Either flexible plastic bags (5) or rigid gas-tight cabinets can be used as anaerobic chambers. Manipulation of the contents of the chamber is done by means of gloves sealed to the chamber. A glove-free anaerobic chamber (Anaerobe Systems) has cuffs around the midarm and leaves hands unencumbered by gloves (Fig 2-7). Material is passed in and out of the chamber through an interchange; the latter is usually a rigid compartment with an inner and outer door and is attached to the chamber by a gas-tight seal. The interchange can be evacuated and refilled by a series of flushes with an oxygen-free gas to quickly make the interchange anaerobic in a manner similar to that described previously for jars; this process has been automated in some chambers. The number of evacuations needed is dependent upon the porosity of the material being processed.

The chamber is made anaerobic initially by evacuating and replacing its atmosphere three to five times with a gas mixture containing 5% to 10% H_2, 5% to 10% CO_2, and 80% to 90% N_2 in the presence of active catalyst. A fresh indicator strip (methylene blue) is opened to test conditions after the first two to three evacuations and replacements. The chamber is anaerobic when the strip remains white.

The chamber itself is kept anaerobic at all times by the use of a palladium catalyst and 3% to 10% H_2 in the atmosphere. A new methylene blue indicator strip should be opened within the chamber every 1 to 2 days or one may open a tube of PRAS peptone yeast extract (PY) broth with resazurin indicator and cap it loosely with aluminum foil. Moisture produced by the catalytic conversion of H_2 and O_2 to water is controlled by its absorption into silica gel crystals with indicator. The dessicant turns from bright blue to pink when water-logged, and is "recharged" by drying in a hot oven.

A comparison of anaerobic methods is given in Table 2-2.

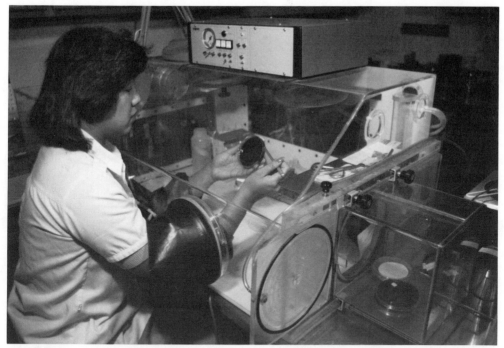

a

b

Fig. 2-7. Anaerobic chambers. a. A rigid, glove-free system. b. A flexible glove system.

Table 2-2 Comparison of culture methods for isolation of anaerobes from clinical specimens.

	PRAS tubes	Anaerobic chamber	Anaerobic jar	Bio-Bag®
Initial cost	Moderate	High	Moderate	Low
Continuing cost	Moderate	Moderate	Moderate	Moderate
Time factor	Moderate	Moderate	Low	Low
Space required	Moderate	Moderate-Large	Moderate	Small
Recovery of significant anaerobes	Satisfactory, but technique cumbersome	Satisfactory, but technique time consuming	Satisfactory and convenient	Satisfactory and convenient
Suitability for tissue grinding, specimen homogenization with blender	Not suitable	Allows processing without exposure to oxygen	Not suitable	Not suitable
Principal advantages	Tubes can be inspected at any time without disturbing anaerobic conditions	Plates can be inspected at any time under anaerobic conditions; conventional isolation procedures are employed	Uncomplicated and convenient; conventional techniques employed	Plates can be inspected at any time without disturbing anaerobic conditions; uncomplicated and convenient; conventional techniques employed
Principal disadvantages	Technique requires more training time; cumbersome to isolate and purify strains; colony morphology frequently not distinctive	Space requirement; high initial cost; time consuming	Possibility of prolonged exposure of plates to oxygen during inspection and subculture	Holds only two plates; possibility of prolonged exposure of plates to oxygen during subculture

CHAPTER 3

PROCESSING CLINICAL SPECIMENS AND ISOLATION AND IDENTIFICATION PROCEDURES

INITIAL PROCESSING PROCEDURE

Properly collected and transported specimens for anaerobic culture may be processed on the bench, in an anaerobic chamber, or with the roll tube system. Initial processing includes direct examination and inoculation of the specimen onto appropriate media as represented in Fig. 3-1.

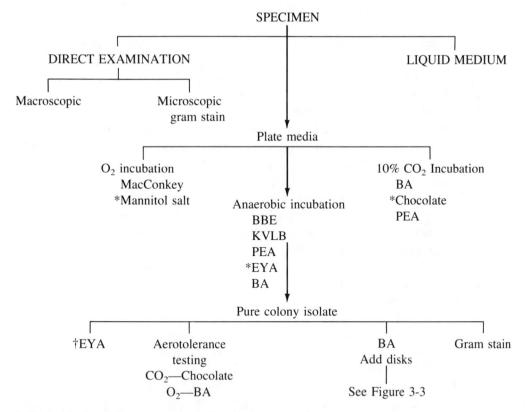

SPECIMEN

DIRECT EXAMINATION   LIQUID MEDIUM

Macroscopic   Microscopic
                     gram stain

Plate media

O_2 incubation   10% CO_2 Incubation
MacConkey   BA
*Mannitol salt   *Chocolate
                                         PEA
              Anaerobic incubation
              BBE
              KVLB
              PEA
              *EYA
              BA

Pure colony isolate

†EYA   Aerotolerance   BA   Gram stain
            testing   Add disks
         CO_2—Chocolate
            O_2—BA   See Figure 3-3

* Optional, depending on specimen source or gram stain
† For suspected lipase producers and all *Clostridium* sp.

Fig. 3-1. Initial processing of specimens

Direct examination

Direct examination involves a macro- and microscopic examination and may include end-product analysis, dark field or fluorescent-antibody screening techniques. The direct examination provides immediate semiquantitative information about the types of organisms present and presumptive evidence that the specimen contains anaerobic bacteria. This is important for initial therapy since culture results may not be available for several days.

The specimen is inspected for characteristics that include: 1) foul odor due to end-products of anaerobic bacteria, especially fusobacteria and pigmented *Bacteroides*; 2) brick red fluorescence due to protoporphyrin production by the pigmented *Bacteroides* sp.; 3) black necrotic tissue or black discharge which may be due to pigmented *Bacteroides* sp.; 4) sulfur granules associated with *Actinomyces* sp., *Arachnia* sp. and other organisms; 5) blood; and 6) purulence.

The microscopic examination always includes a Gram stain. The Gram stain reveals the types and relative number of microorganisms and host cells present and is a quality control measure for the microbiologist. It may also suggest using special media. Failure to recover all the morphotypes seen on the Gram stain smear may indicate a problem in anaerobic techniques (collection, transport, or processing) or, much less commonly, inhibition of the organisms by residual antibiotic. Pale, irregular staining gram-negative bacilli are frequently anaerobic. Coccobacillary forms are suggestive of the pigmenting *Bacteroides* or *Haemophilus* sp. *F. nucleatum* is a thin gram-negative bacillus with pointed ends; this organism is often found in pairs end-to-end. This distinct morphology is shared with the microaerophile *Capnocytophaga* sp. *Leptotrichia buccalis* is a larger fusiform bacillus. An extremely pleomorphic gram-negative bacillus with filaments containing swollen areas, large round bodies, and irregular staining is suggestive of *F. mortiferum*. *F. necrophorum* may have a similar microscopic morphology. A tiny (<0.5 µm diameter) gram-negative coccus is suggestive of *Veillonella* sp. A large gram-positive rod with square ends (boxcar-shaped cells) and no spores may be identified presumptively as *C. perfringens*. A few *Clostridium* sp. usually appear gram-negative. Branching gram-positive bacilli, although suggestive of *Actinomyces*, may be *Corynebacterium*, *Propionibacterium*, *Bifidobacterium*, or *Arachnia*. It is important to correlate specimen source with microscopic morphotypes and to report this presumptive evidence of anaerobic infection to the clinician.

Dark-field or phase-contrast microscopy may aid in detecting poorly staining organisms and spores and in observing motility directly. A two hour direct fluorescent antibody stain (FA) for the *B. fragilis* group (Fluoretec-F) and some pigmented *Bacteroides* sp. (Fluoretec-M) is available (General Diagnostics) and appears to be reliable.

The sensitivity and specificity of Fluoretec-F, according to Weissfeld and Sonnenwirth, is 88% and 87% respectively (175). False-negative FA tests were in part due to *B. ovatus*, *B. vulgatus*, and *B. distasonis* which often give negative FA results with colonies. These same researchers evaluated the Fluoretec-M and found the sensitivity and specificity to be 94% and 92% respectively.

False-positive FA results were partially attributed to improper transport and prior antibiotic therapy. In addition, Fluoretec-M cross-reacts with some strains of *B. bivius* and *B. disiens*, indicating that these organisms share common cell wall antigens with the pigmented *Bacteroides* sp. Mouton *et al.* found that Fluoretec-M was unable to detect *B. levii* and oral strains of *B. asaccharolyticus* (113). The recent taxonomic changes occurring within the pigmented *Bacteroides* group may explain some of the problems with this test kit. These direct fluorescent antibody procedures are time consuming and are recommended only for appropriately equipped laboratories experienced in these techniques.

Direct gas-liquid chromatographic analysis of purulent material for end-products of anaerobic metabolism may provide rapid presumptive evidence for anaerobic infection (59). See Chapter 4 for procedures and discussion. This procedure is rarely used in our laboratory, for we often have not found it useful; we rely more on the presence of a foul odor and gram stain morphology.

Specimen preparation and inoculation

After direct examination, the prepared specimen is inoculated onto appropriate anaerobic and aerobic plating media, into a liquid medium, and onto a slide for Gram stain.

Grossly purulent material is mixed by vortexing in the anaerobic transport vial to ensure even distribution of the organisms. Specimens transported in a syringe are injected into an anaerobic tube for vortexing. Pieces of tissue or bone fragments are homogenized with approximately 1 ml of liquid medium using a tissue grinder to make a thick mixture. Grinding should be done in an anaerobic chamber to minimize aeration. If a chamber is not available, then process the specimen as rapidly as possible. Swab specimens are "wrung out" in about 0.5 ml of broth and treated as a liquid specimen. Using a Pasteur pipet, add the prepared specimen as follows: 1) 1 drop per plate for purulent material; 2) 2 to 3 drops per plate for nonpurulent material; 3) 0.5 to 1 ml to the middle or bottom of the tube of liquid medium; and 4) 1 drop evenly spread onto the slide.

If the swab specimen is inoculated directly onto the media, inoculate the non-selective plates first (both aerobic and anaerobic plates), and then the selective and differential plates. Roll the swab over the first quadrant of each plate, applying as much pressure as possible, but not enough to break through the agar. Next, inoculate the thioglycolate broth by gently introducing the swab into the lower half of the tube and rubbing it against the wall of the tube. "Wring" the swab out just above the fluid level, and then prepare a slide for the Gram stain. It is best to obtain two swabs, one of which can be aerobic and used for the Gram stain, since the swab used to inoculate the media will have fewer organisms than in the original specimen.

The direct smears are methanol-fixed for 30 seconds in order to preserve red and white cell morphology. Standard Gram stain procedures and reagents are used except that basic fuchsin is used as the counterstain. Basic fuchsin enhances staining of the gram-negative anaerobes.

Media. A combination of enriched, nonselective, selective, and differential media is used for the isolation and presumptive identification of bacteria from clinical material.

To determine the appropriate media required for the recovery of aerobic or facultative anaerobic bacteria from various sites, refer to the *Manual of Clinical Microbiology*, *Diagnostic Microbiology*, or any other standard reference source (47,93). Sheep blood, MacConkey, and phenylethyl alcohol blood agar plates are used as a minimum set for primary inoculation.

The following media are used for the primary isolation of obligately anaerobic bacteria:

1) Brucella 5% sheep blood agar supplemented with vitamin K_1 and hemin (BA) for the isolation of all bacteria.
2) Bacteroides bile esculin (BBE) agar for the selection and presumptive identification of *B. fragilis* group organisms (96).
3) Kanamycin-vancomycin laked blood (KVLB) agar for the selection of pigmented and other *Bacteroides* sp. (49).
4) Phenylethyl alcohol sheep blood agar (PEA) for the inhibition of enteric and certain other non-anaerobic gram-negative bacilli which otherwise may overgrow the anaerobes.
5) Thioglycollate medium (BBL-135C) supplemented with vitamin K_1, hemin, and a marble chip or sodium bicarbonate (add prior to use). This serves as a backup culture.

The primary plates are reduced for at least 24 hours prior to use, unless freshly prepared media are used. Prereduced anaerobically sterilized (PRAS) plated media are available (Anaerobe Systems); however, clinical laboratory studies are needed to determine their efficacy. Subsequent BA plates used for subculturing do not need to be reduced (147). The liquid medium is boiled or steamed to drive off residual oxygen and is used on the day of steaming.

Columbia, Schaedler, or brain heart infusion supplemented with 0.5% yeast extract, may also be used for the blood agar base. Unsupplemented tryptic soy and heart infusion or brain-heart infusion agar plates, used for isolation of aerobic bacteria, do not adequately support the growth of all anaerobes. The following supplements are added to the bases: 1) 5% sheep, horse, or rabbit blood for enrichment and for detecting hemolysis, 2) vitamin K_1 (final concentration 10 μg/ml) for growth of some pigmented *Bacteroides*, and 3) hemin (final concentration 5 μg/ml) for growth enhancement of the *B. fragilis* group and other *Bacteroides* sp. (146).

The BBE agar is useful for the rapid isolation and presumptive identification of the *B. fragilis* group. It contains 100 μg/ml of gentamicin which inhibits most anaerobic organisms, 20% bile, which inhibits most *Bacteroides* except for the *B. fragilis* group and a few other species; and esculin, which aids in detecting the *B. fragilis* group which are usually esculin positive. Other non-*B. fragilis* group organisms that may rarely grow on this medium are *F. mortiferum*, *K. pneumoniae*, enterococcus, and yeast. However, unlike the *B. fragilis* group, their colony size is usually less than 1 mm in diameter.

The KVLB agar is useful for the rapid isolation of *Bacteroides* sp. The medium contains 75 μg/ml kanamycin which inhibits most aerobic, facultative, and anaerobic gram-negative rods except for *Bacteroides* and 7.5 μg/ml vancomycin which inhibits most gram-positive organisms. The laked blood allows earlier pigmentation of the pigmented *Bacteroides* sp. However, many strains of *B. asaccharolyticus* and *B. gingivalis* will not grow on this medium because of their susceptibility to vancomycin. Yeast and other kanamycin-resistant organisms sometimes grow on this medium; therefore, one should Gram stain and determine the aerotolerance of all isolates.

The PEA agar inhibits non-anaerobic gram-negative rods. It prevents *Proteus* sp. from swarming and other enterics from overgrowing the anaerobes. Most gram-positive and gram-negative anaerobes will grow on the primary PEA plates, especially in mixed culture, and the colony morphology is similar to that on blood agar; however, it may take an additional 48 hours incubation to detect the more slowly growing and pigmenting anaerobes.

The thioglycolate broth serves only as a backup source of culture material, which may be needed in the event of a jar failure or growth inhibition on plates due to antibiotic or bacteriostatic factors (e.g., penicillin, polymorphonuclear leukocytes) in the specimen; these factors will be diluted out in the broth.

If clostridia are suspected clinically or from the Gram stain (spores or large gram-positive rods) of the clinical material, an egg yolk agar (EYA) plate is also inoculated to check for the production of lecithinase and lipase. If box car shaped cells resembling *C. perfringens* are seen on Gram stain, a direct Nagler test can also be set up along with the primary plates. If fusobacteria are suspected, a *Fusobacterium* egg yolk agar (FEA) plate may be inoculated (112). (Other selective and non-selective media that may be used in the initial processing are listed in tables A-1 to A-3 in the Appendix.)

INCUBATION OF CULTURES

Inoculated plates are streaked into quadrants for isolation, are immediately placed into an anaerobic environment (jars, chamber, Bio-Bag type A), and are incubated at 35°C for 48 hours. If plates are inoculated on the bench and incubated in jars, the cultures must not be exposed to oxygen until after 48 hours of incubation, since anaerobes are most sensitive to oxygen during their log phase of growth. Plates incubated in a chamber or Bio-Bag can be inspected at 24 hours or earlier for the presence of *B. fragilis* group on the BBE plate and *Clostridium* sp. on the BA or EYA plates. Isolates from the BBE and EYA may be worked up at 24 hours or when good growth is evident. The BA plate incubated in a Bio-Bag should also be held 48 hours prior to workup. Plates incubated in a chamber may be worked up at any time; it is recommended that only large colonies on the BA be further processed at 24 hours, as colony size and morphology will vary greatly from the 24 to 48 hours inspection.

Negative culture plates are held for seven days before final examination. The thioglycolate broth of a negative culture is inspected daily for seven days and, when turbid or on day seven, subcultured to a BA plate (anaerobic incubation) and a chocolate agar plate (CO_2 incubation). Although a final report of a negative culture is issued at seven days, the liquid medium is held for at least one more week before a final visual examination and discarding.

EXAMINATION OF CULTURE AND ISOLATION OF ANAEROBES

Anaerobes are usually present in mixed culture with other anaerobes or with facultative bacteria. It is important to work up all colony morphotypes from the nonselective media, since facultative and anaerobic bacteria sometimes have similar colony appearances. Clues to the presence of anaerobes in the culture include a foul odor upon opening an anaerobic jar, more colony types present on the anaerobically incubated BA plate than on the CO_2 incubated BA plate, growth on the BBE plate, and brick red fluorescing or black-pigmented colonies on the KVLB or BA.

Examination of primary plates

Primary anaerobic plates should be examined with a hand lens (8x) or a stereoscopic microscope. Colonies are described from the various media, as listed below, and semiquantitated. The quantity may be described as light, moderate, or heavy, or by the number of quadrants in which growth appears (1+, 2+, 3+, 4+ growth).

All colony types growing on the BA plate are described, semiquantitated and subcultured. A detailed colony description is recorded; this includes size, shape, edge, profile, color, opacity, hemolysis, fluorescence, pigment, pitting and any other noteworthy characteristics. Pitting colonies present on the anaerobic but not the CO_2 plate are suggestive of the *B. ureolyticus*-like group. Large colonies with a double zone of beta-hemolysis made up of large gram-positive rods are presumptively *C. perfringens*. These colonies may be subcultured additionally to an egg yolk agar plate for the Nagler test. Breadcrumb-like or speckled colonies with greening of the agar around the colonies that subsequently are shown to be slender fusiform gram-negative bacilli suggest *F. nucleatum*. Dark pigmented or brick red fluorescent colonies that are gram-negative coccobacilli are pigmented *Bacteroides* sp. A molar tooth colony of gram-positive branching rods may be *Actinomyces* sp.

Only those colonies growing on the BBE plates that are greater than 1 mm in diameter should be described, enumerated, and subcultured. The *B. fragilis* group are >1 mm in diameter, circular, entire, and raised, and there are 3 distinct morphotypes: 1) low convex, dark grey, friable, and surrounded by a dark-grey zone and a precipitate; 2) glistening, convex, light to dark grey and surrounded by a grey zone; or 3) similar to the second morphotype, but no grey zone.

All colony types are subcultured from the KVLB plate and carefully checked for pigment (this may take >48 hours to appear) and brick red fluorescence which is detected with UV light (366 nm).

Colonies on the PEA plate are further processed if they are different from ones growing on the BA plate or if the BA plate is impossible to pick from because of overgrowth by swarming *Proteus*, clostridia, or other organisms.

Subculture of isolates

Only one colony of each type described is Gram-stained and subcultured to the following:

1) BA plate to be incubated anaerobically for isolation of the organism and subsequent testing.
2) Chocolate agar plate to be incubated in CO_2 for aerotolerance testing.
3) BA plate to be incubated in room air for aerotolerance testing (optional).
4) EYA plate for suspected lipase and lecithinase producers (*Clostridium* sp., *F. necrophorum, B. intermedius*) — optional.
5) Rabbit blood (preferably laked) agar (RBA) plate for better detection of pigment production.

Four to six isolates can be inoculated onto an EYA plate, and many can be inoculated onto the CO_2 chocolate agar, aerobic BA aerotolerance, and RBA plates. A sterile wooden stick is used for transferring because it picks up the colony and retains enough material for inoculation of multiple plates and can then be rubbed onto a slide, without water, for Gram stain.

The first quadrant of the purity BA plate is streaked back and forth several times to ensure an even lawn of heavy growth; the other quadrants are streaked for isolation. The following special potency antibiotic disks are placed as shown in Fig. 3-2: kanamycin, 1 mg (BBL); colistin, 10 μg; and vancomycin, 5 μg.

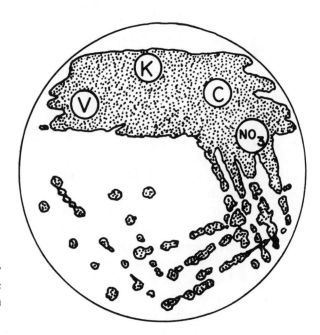

Fig. 3-2. Diagram of purity plate with antibiotic and other disks in place.

These disks aid in preliminary grouping of anaerobes and serve as a Gram stain check, but do *not* imply susceptibility of an organism for antibiotic therapy (159). A sodium polyanethol sulfonate (SPS) disk can be placed near the colistin disk for rapid identification of *P. anaerobius* (179). A nitrate disk may be placed on the second quadrant for subsequent determination of nitrate reduction (178). Alternatively, these latter two disks may be used later on selected isolates rather than all isolates.

The chocolate agar plate incubated in a 5% to 10% CO_2 atmosphere for 48 hours is required for aerotolerance testing in order to detect slow growing, fastidious facultative organisms that do not grow alone on blood agar plates (e.g., *Haemophilus*) or that require CO_2. Use of a BA plate for CO_2 incubation alone may give a false-negative aerotolerance test. An additional BA plate incubated in air will further define the atmospheric requirements of facultative organisms (e.g., microaerophilic streptococci). Some gram-positive organisms considered to be anaerobes can grow in a 10% CO_2-enriched ambient atmosphere and may be aerotolerant enough to grow poorly in air. *A. israelii*, *A. naeslundii*, *A. odontolyticus*, *A. propionica*, and a few *Propionibacterium* sp., *Bifidobacterium* sp., and *Lactobacillus* sp. are microaerophilic bacteria usually considered in discussions of anaerobes. Several species of *Clostridium*, including *C. carnis*, *C. haemolyticum*, and *C. tertium* will grow but not sporulate in air. Conversely, some streptococci require several subcultures before they grow in a CO_2 atmosphere.

The same colony subcultured to the purity plate must be used for aerotolerance testing and the Gram stain. If the original colony is not large enough to determine atmospheric requirements directly, then use growth from the purity plate for aerotolerance testing. If the subculture is mixed, it must be reisolated and retested for atmospheric requirement.

If the processing is done on the open bench, all anaerobic plates should be promptly incubated (within 30 minutes), since some clinical isolates may die after relatively short exposure to oxygen (e.g., *F. necrophorum*, pigmented *Bacteroides* sp.). The primary plates are reincubated along with the purity plates for an additional 48 hours, and are again inspected for new morphotypes of slow growers and pigmenters.

IDENTIFICATION OF ISOLATES
General Considerations

Pure culture isolates of anaerobes are further processed for identification as shown in Fig. 3-3. The Wadsworth Anaerobic Bacteriology Laboratory is committed to as complete an identification as possible for all anaerobes isolated. For a variety of reasons including time, material, and personnel considerations — this philosophy is not practical for all laboratories. There are three levels at which laboratories can operate with regard to anaerobic workup. All laboratories should be capable of functioning at Level I: presumptive identification from primary plates, isolation and maintenance of an anaerobe in pure culture so that in important clinical cases the isolate can be sent to a reference laboratory for

PURE CULTURE BA WITH DISKS

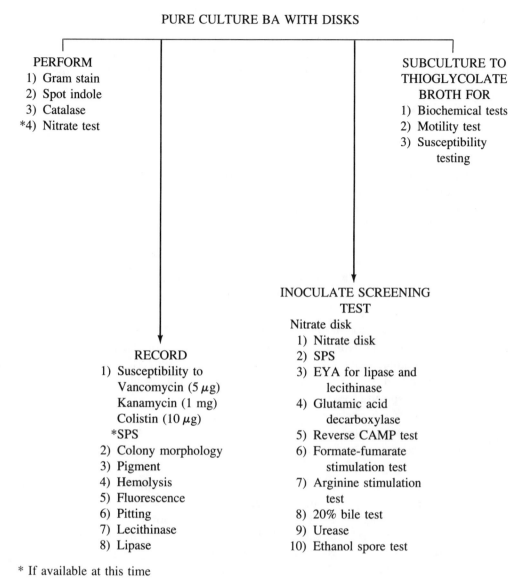

PERFORM
1) Gram stain
2) Spot indole
3) Catalase
*4) Nitrate test

SUBCULTURE TO
THIOGLYCOLATE
BROTH FOR
1) Biochemical tests
2) Motility test
3) Susceptibility
   testing

INOCULATE SCREENING
TEST
Nitrate disk
1) Nitrate disk
2) SPS
3) EYA for lipase and
   lecithinase
4) Glutamic acid
   decarboxylase
5) Reverse CAMP test
6) Formate-fumarate
   stimulation test
7) Arginine stimulation
   test
8) 20% bile test
9) Urease
10) Ethanol spore test

RECORD
1) Susceptibility to
   Vancomycin (5 μg)
   Kanamycin (1 mg)
   Colistin (10 μg)
   *SPS
2) Colony morphology
3) Pigment
4) Hemolysis
5) Fluorescence
6) Pitting
7) Lecithinase
8) Lipase

* If available at this time

Fig. 3-3. Diagrammatic scheme for identifying anaerobes.

complete identification and susceptibility testing. Level II laboratories will use simple tests to further group the anaerobes and speciate certain ones. Level III laboratories will identify the anaerobes isolated as completely as possible using a variety of techniques that may include PRAS biochemicals, miniaturized biochemical systems (e.g., API and Minitek), CDC thioglycolate biochemicals, rapid enzyme detection panels (IDS), gas-liquid chromatography, toxin assays, etc.

Level I Identification

Information from the primary plates in conjunction with the atmospheric requirements, Gram stain, and colonial morphology of a pure isolate provides presumptive identification of anaerobic organisms. Table 3-1 summarizes the extent to which isolates can be identified using information from the primary plates, Gram stain, and aerotolerance testing.

Level II Identification

General considerations. Preliminary grouping of anaerobes and speciation of some are based on colonial and cellular morphology (Fig. 3-4, Fig. 3-5). Gram reaction, susceptibility to special potency antibiotic and nitrate disks, indole, catalase, and other simple tests (Fig. 3-6). The following characteristics are noted and tests made from the purity BA plate on *all* isolates as depicted schematically in Fig. 3-3:

1. Colony morphology is again described in detail; this includes colony size, shape, color, internal appearance, profile, opacity, general appearance (e.g., mucoid, glistening, breadcrumb-like, dull), and other distinctive characteristics.
2. Hemolysis. Use transmitted light to look for beta-hemolysis, a double zone of beta-hemolysis (clear zone of hemolysis extending just beyond the colonies and a zone of partial hemolysis extending well beyond the colony edge), and greening of the agar which usually is more apparent after exposure to air.
3. Pigment. Colors common among certain anaerobes vary from light tan to black (pigmented *Bacteroides* sp.) or pink to red (*A. odontolyticus*). It is sometimes helpful to pick up several colonies on a swab for easier detection of pigment.
4. Pitting. The BA plate must often be held at an angle to the light source to detect corroding of the agar surrounding the colony. This characteristic may be easier to detect after four days of incubation.
5. Fluorescence. Long wave UV light is used to detect fluorescing colonies. A variety of colors may be seen including brick red, pink, and chartreuse (yellow-green) (144).
6. Catalase. Colonies harvested on a stick from a BA culture are placed in a drop of 15% hydrogen peroxide. The evolution of bubbles denotes a positive test. Avoid picking up blood agar because a false-positive test may result because of catalase in the red blood cells. If this is not possible, streak the organism to a blood-free medium (such as EYA) and then perform the test. It is not necessary to expose plates to oxygen prior to testing for catalase production. Carbohydrate-containing media may repress catalase activity (181).
7. Indole. Growth from a tryptophane-containing medium (BA) is rubbed onto filter paper saturated with paradimethylaminocinnamaldehyde reagent. A blue color denotes a positive test. It is important to use a pure culture because indole is diffusible.

Legend for Table of Characteristics
Aerotolerance
    A = Anaerobic
    M = Microaerophilic
    F = Facultative
Morphology
    B = Bacillus
    CB = Coccobacillus
    C = Coccus
Susceptibility
    R = Resistant
    S = Susceptible
Reactions
    − = Negative reaction
    + = Positive reaction for majority of strains; includes weak as well as strong acid
      production from carbohydrates in saccharolytic organisms
    $+^-$ = Most strains positive, reaction helpful if positive
    $+^w$ = Most strains positive, some weakly positive
    w^- = Most strains weakly positive, some negative
    $-^+$ = Most strains negative, some weakly positive
    $-^w$ = Most strains negative, some weakly positive
    (+) = Delayed reaction
    C = Clot formed in milk
    D = Milk digested
    V = Variable reaction
    PRAS carbohydrates: + pH,<5.5
                                  W pH,5.5-5.7
                                    − pH,>5.7
Note: if pH of base medium is below 6.0, pH of test must drop 0.3 units to be "weak"
Gas in PYG agar deep: —, no gas detected
                               2, splits agar horizontally
                               3, agar displaced halfway to top of the tube
                               4, agar displaced to top of the tube
Fatty acids

A	=	Acetic	IC	=	Isocaproic
P	=	Propionic	C	=	Caproic
IB	=	Isobutyric	C′	=	Caprylic
B	=	Butyric	L	=	Lactic
IV	=	Isovaleric	S	=	Succinic
V	=	Valeric	PA	=	Phenylacetic

Note: 1) Capital letters indicate major metabolic products
       2) Small letters indicate minor products
       3) Parentheses indicate a variable reaction
       4) Isoacids are primarily from carbohydrate-free media (such as PY)
          in the case of saccharolytic organisms

NOTES:

Table 3-1 Level I identification

	Cell shape	Gram reac- tion	Aero- toler- ance	Distinguishing characteristics
B. fragilis group	B	—	—	growth on BBE with colony size > 1 mm in diameter
Pigmented *Bacteroides* sp.	CB B	—	—	dark pigmenting or brick red fluorescing colony
B. ureolyticus-like group	B	—	—	pitting colonies
F. nucleatum (presumptive)	B	—	—	slender bacillus with pointed ends; breadcrumbs, speckling colony
Anaerobic gram-negative bacillus	B CB	—	—	
Anaerobic gram-negative coccus	C	—	—	
Anaerobic gram-positive coccus	C	+	—	
C. perfringens (presumptive)	B	+	—	double zone of beta hemolysis boxcar shaped cells
Other *Clostridium* sp.	B	+	—⁺	spores seen on Gram stain
Anaerobic gram-positive bacillus	B	+	—⁺	no boxcar shaped cells, no spores

8. Special potency antibiotic disc susceptibility. Colistin (10 μg), vancomy-cin (5 μg), and kanamycin (1 mg) disks are placed on the first quadrant of a well-streaked purity BA plate. A zone size of 10 mm or less is con-sidered resistant. The disks are used as an aid in determining the Gram reaction and in separating the *Bacteroides* and *Fusobacterium* species. Generally, gram-positive organisms are resistant to colistin and sensitive to vancomycin, whereas the gram-negative organisms are resistant to vancomycin. This is especially helpful with those clostridia that consis-tently stain gram-negative. Some exceptions do occur, including certain members of the pigmented *Bacteroides* sp., and will be discussed in a

Fig. 3-4. Colonial morphology

 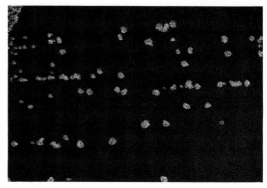

a. *F. necrophorum:* note umbonate profile and pleomorphic colonies.
b. *F. nucleatum:* note breadcrumb colony - dry, irregular, white; greening of agar

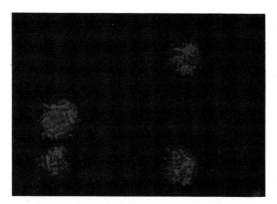 

c. *F. nucleatum:* note speckling colony - circular, entire, gray; greening of agar
d. *B. ureolyticus;* note pitting

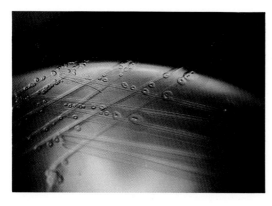 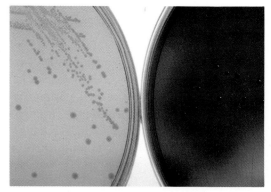

e. *B. ureolyticus:* higher magnification of d.
f. *B. fragilis* (left) vs. *B. vulgatus* on BBE: note difference in esculin reaction (blackening)

Fig. 3-4. Colonial morphology (cont.)

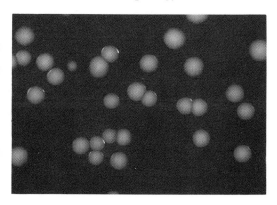

g. *B. fragilis:* colonies on BA
h. *B. intermedius:* pigmentation on sheep (L) and rabbit (R) blood agars

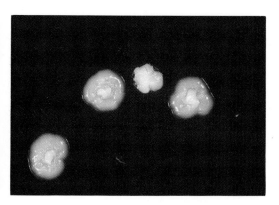

i. *A. israelii:* note molar-tooth shape
j. *C. septicum:* note "medusa-head" colony at 6-8 h

k. *C. perfringens:* note double zone of beta-hemolysis (inner zone is under colony only)
l. *C. difficile:* note typical ground-glass appearance and yellow colonies on CCFA

Fig. 3-5. Microscopic morphology

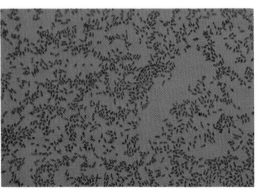 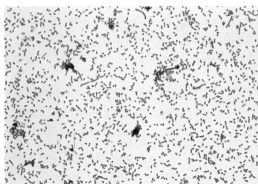

a. *B. fragilis:* uniform width, varied length
b. Pigmented *Bacteroides* sp: many coccobacillary forms with some rod shaped forms interspersed

 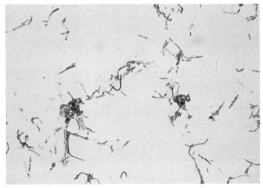

c. *F. nucleatum:* thin gram-negative bacillus with pointed ends
d. *F. necrophorum:* note pleomorphism and swollen forms which may be similar to *F. mortiferum*

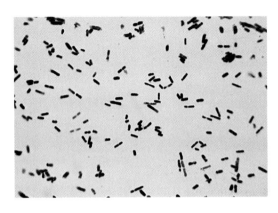

e. *C. perfringens:* box-car shaped cells; gram variable; absence of spores

Fig. 3-5. Microscopic morphology (cont.)

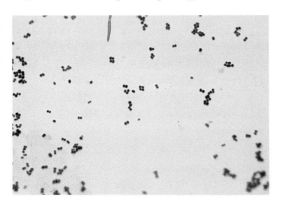 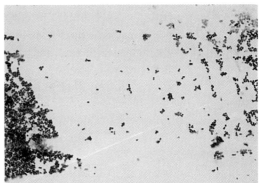

f. *P. magnus* (left) vs. *P. micros:* Note larger size of *P. magnus* and chain formation of *P. micros*

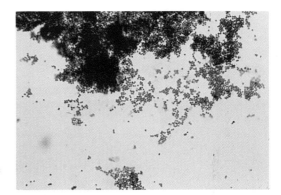

g. *Veillonella:* small gram-negative coccus

h. *P. anaerobius:* large coccobacillary cells which form chains

later section. *Fusobacterium* species are susceptible to both kanamycin and colistin, and *Bacteroides* are generally resistant to kanamycin, but variable in susceptibility to colistin.

The following additional tests are performed on certain isolates (Fig. 3-6). The principle and use of each test is discussed in the Appendix.

1. Ethanol spore test (88).Test gram-positive rods to differentiate *Clostridium* sp. from other gram-positive rods. It is not necessary to perform the test on isolates of *C. perfringens*, *C. ramosum*, or *C. clostridiiforme*.

2. 20% bile test. This test is important for the gram-negative bacilli, since the *B. fragilis* group and some *Fusobacterium* are not inhibited by 20% bile.

3. Lecithinase. All clostridia are tested for lecithinase production.

4. Lipase. All clostridia, pigmented *Bacteroides*, and fusobacteria are tested for lipase production.

5. Reverse CAMP test (24, 65). Test all suspected *C. perfringens*.

6. Nagler reaction (alternative to reverse CAMP test). Test *C. perfringens*-like colonies. There are only four Nagler-positive clostridia, including *C. perfringens*.

7. Urease. Nagler-positive clostridia and *B. ureolyticus*-like organisms are tested.

Fig. 3-6. Level II tests

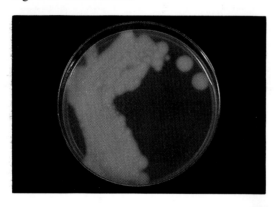

a. Lecithinase reaction: note opacity of agar due to precipitation of complex fats.

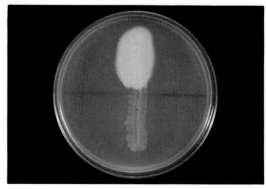

b. *C. perfringens* demonstrating a positive Nagler test.

Fig. 3-6. Level II tests (cont.)

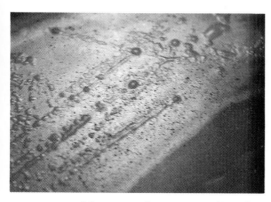
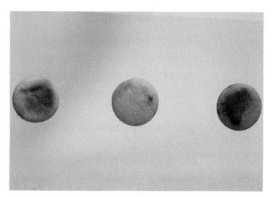

  c. Lipase reaction: note mother-of-pearl sheen
  d. Spot indole test using para-dimethylaminocinnamaldehyde: blue or blue-green = positive; colorless, or other than blue = negative

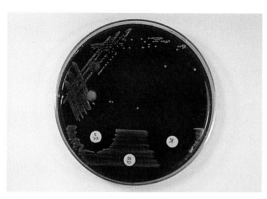
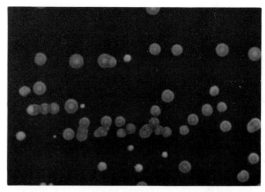

  e. *P. acnes* on BA demonstrating positive spot indole and nitrate reactions. Note typical antibiotic disk pattern for a gram positive organism: colistin = R; vancomycin = S. Also note the typical early colony morphology showing small white opaque colonies
  f. Brick red fluorescence (long wave UV light) of a pigmented *Bacteroides* sp.

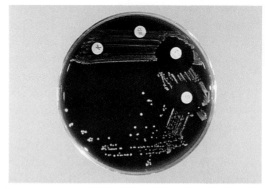

  g. *C. perfringens* and Group B beta-hemolytic streptococcus showing a positive reverse CAMP test
  h. *P. anaerobius* with a positive SPS test (S disk). Note the fairly large size of the colonies

8. Nitrate disk test. Test tiny indole-negative gram-positive rods (*Eubacterium lentum*-like), *B. ureolyticus*-like organisms, and gram-negative cocci.
9. Sodium polyanethol sulfonate (SPS). Test gram-positive cocci that morphologically and microscopically resemble *P. anaerobius* (large cocci in chains, foul odor).
10. Glutamic acid decarboxylase (53,78). Test Nagler-positive, indole-positive clostridia.
11. Formate and fumarate (F/F) growth stimulation test. Test gram-negative rods that form small transparent colonies and are susceptible to both colistin and kanamycin.
12. Arginine growth stimulation test. Test all small gram-positive bacilli not resembling diphtheroids.
13. Motility. Test *B. ureolyticus*-like bacilli and other gram-negative bacilli that do not key out if assumed to be non-motile.

Several of these tests are incorporated in the Lombard-Dowell Presumpto 1 plate which is available from many sources (35). The more fastidious organisms (certain pigmenters, cocci, *Fusobacterium*) do not grow well on the basal medium and some manufacturers supplement it. Good growth on the basal medium is required to accurately interpret results.

Level II group identification. Tables 3-2 and 3-3 divide the anaerobes by Gram reaction and show the major groups and readily speciable anaerobes within those groups.

The gram-negative organisms are divided into the following major categories based on microscopic morphology, special potency antibiotic disk patterns, or other simple tests: 1) *B. fragilis* group, 2) pigmented *Bacteroides* sp., 3) *B. ureolyticus*-like group (formate/fumarate requirers), 4) other *Bacteroides* sp., 5) *Fusobacterium* sp., and 6) anaerobic gram-negative cocci which include *Veillonella*, *Megasphaera*, and *Acidaminococcus*.

The special potency antibiotic disks can be used to separate the gram-negative rods into *Bacteroides* or *Fusobacterium* sp. The *Bacteroides* are resistant to vancomycin (as are most gram-negative anaerobes) and kanamycin, and are variable in susceptibility to colistin. The *Fusobacterium* sp. are resistant to vancomycin and susceptible to both colistin and kanamycin. Exceptions to this generalization include certain black-pigmented *Bacteroides* and the *B. ureolyticus*-like group. *B. asaccharolyticus* and *B. gingivalis* are usually susceptible to vancomycin and resistant to colistin and kanamycin. *B. ureolyticus, B. gracilis,* and *Wolinella* sp. have the same pattern as fusobacteria; however, their colonies are much smaller and more translucent.

An anaerobic gram-negative bacillus that requires formate and fumarate for growth in broth culture may be identified presumptively as a *B. ureolyticus*-like organism. Organisms that fluoresce brick red or produce black colonies are placed in the pigmented *Bacteroides* group. The *B. fragilis* group can be identified presumptively by the special potency antibiotic disk pattern (resistant to all three antibiotics) and growth in a 20% bile (or 2% Oxgall) tube test, bile disk test, or on BBE (38, 174). *Bacteroides* sp. is applied to those organisms not fitting the *B. fragilis* group, pigmented *Bacteroides* sp., the *B. ureolyticus*-like group, or *Fusobacterium* sp.

The gram-positive organisms are divided into the following three major categories based on microscopic morphology and the presence of spores: 1) anaerobic gram-positive cocci, which includes *Peptostreptococcus* and *Streptococcus*, 2) *Clostridium*, the anaerobic sporeforming bacilli which are either Nagler-positive or negative, and 3) anaerobic nonsporeforming bacilli which include *Actinomyces, Arachnia, Propionibacterium, Bifidobacterium,* and *Eubacterium*.

Gram-positive organisms that stain gram-negative can be separated from the true gram-negatives with the special potency antibiotic disks. Gram-positive organisms are resistant to colistin and susceptible to vancomycin, whereas the gram-negatives are resistant to vancomycin with the exceptions noted previously. If spores are not present on a Gram stain of the organism, then the ethanol or heat-spore test will separate *Clostridium* sp. from the anaerobic nonsporeforming bacilli. It is impossible to differentiate this latter group accurately to the genus level without end-product analysis, except for *P. acnes* and *E. lentum*.

Level II speciation. The readily speciated anaerobic organisms are shown in Tables 3-2 and 3-3. It is necessary that all stated characteristics are present in order to speciate the following anaerobes. If a characteristic is not present, only a group name can be applied, unless further biochemical testing is carried out.

B. ureolyticus, B. gracilis, and *Wolinella* sp. are thin gram-negative rods with round ends and are susceptible to colistin and kanamycin. The colonies are small, translucent, or transparent, and may produce greening of the agar. Three colony morphotypes exist: smooth and convex, pitting, and spreading. All three can occur in the same culture. The organisms are asaccharolytic, nitrate or nitrite positive, and require formate and fumarate for growth in broth culture. Hydrogen can substitute for formate. The *Wolinella* sp. are motile; *B. ureolyticus* is urease positive; and *B. gracilis* is non-motile and urease negative (166).

An indole positive and lipase positive gram-negative coccobacillus that forms dark pigmented colonies or fluoresces brick red may be identified as *B. intermedius*. Lipase negative strains must be identified using other biochemical tests. A lipase positive, indole negative pigmented *Bacteroides* has been identified as *B. loescheii* (71). We have encountered only one lipase-positive strain of *B. loescheii* in a clinical specimen.

F. nucleatum is an indole positive thin rod with pointed ends. It fluoresces chartreuse and produces greening of the agar upon exposure to air. There are three colony morphotypes of *F. nucleatum*: speckled, breadcrumb-like, and smooth. The colony size varies from <0.5 to 2 mm. The breadcrumb colony is white; the speckled and smooth types are grey to grey-white. A lipase positive *Fusobacterium* is *F. necrophorum*. It is a pleomorphic rod with rounded ends and sometimes bizarre shapes. It is indole positive, fluoresces chartreuse, and produces greening of the agar. The colonies are umbonate, and range in size

Table 3-2 Level II group and species identification of anaerobic gram-negative organisms

	Cell shape	Slender cells with pointed ends	Kanamycin (1 mg)	Vancomycin (5 μg)	Colistin (10 μg)	Growth in 20% bile	Catalase	Indole production	Lipase	Growth stimulated by formate-fumarate	Nitrate reduction	Urease	Motility	Pitting	Pigment	Brick red fluorescence
B. fragilis group	B		R	R	R	+	V	V	−							−
Other *Bacteroides* sp.	B		R	R	V	−	−	V	−		−/+					−
Pigmented *Bacteroides* sp.	CB/B		R	V	V	−	−	V	V						+	+/−
B. intermedius			R	R	S	−	−	+	+/−							
B. loescheii			R	R	V	−	−	−	+/−							−
B. ureolyticus-like group	B		S	R	S	−	−	−	−	+	+	V	V	V		
B. ureolyticus			S	R	S	−	−	−		+	+	+	V	V		
B. gracilis			S	R	S	−		−		+	+	−	−	V		
Wolinella sp.			S	R	S	−		−		+	+	−	−	V		−
Fusobacterium sp.	B	V	S	R	S	V	−	V	V				+			−
F. nucleatum		+	S	R	S	−		+	−							
F. necrophorum		−	S	R	S	+/−		+	+/−							
F. varium-mortiferum		−	S	R	S	+		V	−							
Gram-negative coccus	C		S	R	S						V					+/−
Veillonella sp.	C		S	R	S						+					−

Table 3-3 Level II group and species identification of anaerobic gram-positive organisms

	Cellular morphology	Survives ethanol spore test	Kanamycin (1 mg)	Colistin (10 µg)	Vancomycin (5 µg)	Sodium polyanethol sulfonate (SPS)	Indole production	Nitrate production	Catalase	Arginine stimulation	Lecithinase	Reverse CAMP test	Boxcar shaped cells	Double zone beta-hemolysis	Urease	Ground glass yellow colonies on CCFA medium
Anaerobic gram positive coccus	C	–	V	R	S	V	V	–⁺	V							
P. anaerobius	C/CB	–	Rˢ	R	S	S	–									
P. asaccharolyticus	C	–	S	R	S	R	+									
Clostridium species	B	+	V	R	S						V					
Nagler positive Clostridium sp.	B	+	S	R	S						+					
C. perfringens	B	+	S	R	S		–				+	+	+	+		
C. bifermentans	B	+	S	R	S		+				+	–	–	–	–	
C. sordellii	B	+	S	R	S		+				+	–	–	–	+⁻	
Nagler negative Clostridium sp.	B	+	S	R	S						V					
C. difficile	B	+	S	R	S											+
Nonsporeforming bacilli	CB/B	–	S	R	S											
P. acnes	B	–	S	R	S		+⁻	+⁻	+⁻							
E. lentum	CB/B	–	S	R	S		–	+	–	+						

from 0.5 to 2 mm. Lipase positive strains are often beta-hemolytic. Lipase negative strains require further biochemical tests for identification. A bile resistant
Fusobacterium may be identified tentatively as *F. mortiferum-varium* group.
Other species of *Fusobacterium* (e.g., *F. necrophorum*) may grow in 20% bile;
therefore, further testing is required to confirm the presumptive identification.

A gram-negative coccus <0.5 μm in diameter that reduces nitrate or nitrite is
Veillonella sp. The other gram-negative cocci do not reduce nitrate. Catalase is
variable. The colonies are small and almost transparent.

A gram-positive coccus sensitive to sodium polyanethol sulfonate (SPS) is *P.
anaerobius*. It is a large coccobacillus and usually occurs in chains. The colonies
vary in size from 0.5 to 2/mm in diameter (larger than most anaerobic cocci),
and are grey-white and opaque. A sweet, fetid odor is associated with this organism. An indole positive, gram-positive coccus is *P. asaccharolyticus*. *P. indolicus* , another indole positive coccus, is rarely isolated from clinical specimens;
unlike *P. asaccharolyticus*, it converts lactate to propionate, and is usually nitrate positive and coagulase positive (139).

C. perfringens is a box car shaped gram-positive rod that is lecithinase and
Nagler positive. Most strains show a typical double zone of beta-hemolysis.
Hemolysis may be enhanced by exposure to cold. It is not necessary to demonstrate
spores or spore production by *C. perfringens*. *C. perfringens* is usually reverse
CAMP test positive, whereas other clostridia have been reported negative
(24, 65). The reverse CAMP negative strains are identified with other biochemical
tests. *C. sordelli* and *C. bifermentans* are indole positive and Nagler positive.
C. sordellii is usually urease positive and *C. bifermentans* is negative.

An indole positive, catalase positive, small pleomorphic (diphtheroid-like)
gram-positive bacillus is *P. acnes*. It usually reduces nitrate. The colonies are
initially small and white, and become larger and more yellowish-tan. Indole or
catalase negative strains are identified with more extensive biochemical tests.

A nitrate positive, small gram-positive bacillus whose growth is stimulated
by arginine is identified as *E. lentum*. The colonies are small, grey, and translucent.

Level III Identification

General considerations. In addition to tests performed in Level II, speciation
may require additional biochemical tests and metabolic end-product analysis by
gas-liquid chromatography. Differentiation of genera of anaerobes is shown in
Table 3-4. Recent changes in nomenclature are shown in Table 3-5. Anaerobes
will be subdivided and discussed as follows: 1) gram-negative bacilli (Tables 3-6
to 3-9); 2) gram-negative cocci (Table 3-10); 3) gram-positive cocci (Table
3-11); 4) *Clostridium* sp. (Tables 3-12 and 3-13); 5) gram-positive non-spore-
forming bacilli (Table 3-14).

Level III identification tables show key characteristics for the listed organisms and are based on reactions using PRAS liquid media (see Level III
Identification Systems). A battery of additional tests to be inoculated for each
anaerobe type is listed in Table 3-15. Consult Tables 3-6 to 3-14 and the *VPI*

Table 3-4 Differentiation of genera of anaerobes

Gram-Negative Bacilli
  I. Non-motile or peritrichous flagella
     A. Produce butyric acid (without isobutyric   *Fusobacterium*
         and isovaleric acids)
     B. Produce major lactic acid   *Leptotrichia*
     C. Produce acetic acid and hydrogen sulfide;   *Desulfomonas*
         reduce sulfate
     D. Not as above (A,B,C)   *Bacteroides*
  II. Polar flagella
     A. Fermentative
        1. Produce butyric acid   *Butyrivibrio*
        2. Produce succinic acid
           a. Spiral shaped cells   *Succinivibrio*
           b. Ovoid cells   *Succinimonas*
        3. Produce propionic and acetic acids   *Anaerovibrio*
     B. Non-fermentative; produce succinic acid   *Wolinella*
         from fumarate
 III. Tufts of flagella on concave side of curved cells
     A. Fermentative   *Selenomonas*
     B. Non-fermentative   *Mobiluncus*
 IV. Bipolar tufts of flagella   *Anaerobiospirillum*
Gram-Negative Cocci
  I. Produce propionic and acetic acids   *Veillonella*
  II. Produce butyric and acetic acids   *Acidaminococcus*
 III. Produce isobutyric, butyric, isovaleric,   *Megasphaera*
     valeric, and caproic acids
Gram-Positive Cocci
  I. Require a fermentable carbohydrate
     A. Produce butyric (plus other acids)   *Coprococcus*
     B. Do not produce butyric acid   *Ruminococcus*
  II. Do not require a fermentable carbohydrate
     A. Lactic acid sole major product   *Streptococcus*
     B. Not as above   *Peptostreptococcus*
                                    or *Peptococcus*

Sporeforming Bacilli   *Clostridium*
Gram-Positive Nonsporeforming Bacilli
  I. Produce propionic and acetic acids as major products
     A. Catalase usually positive   *Propionibacterium*
     B. Catalase negative   *Arachnia*
  II. No propionic acid produced
     A. Produce acetic and lactic acids (A>L)   *Bifidobacterium*
     B. Produce lactic acid as sole major end product *Lactobacillus*
     C. Produce moderate acetic acid plus one of the following:
        1. major succinic and lactic acids
        2. major succinic acid   *Actinomyces*
     D. Other: butyric ± others, acetic or
        no major acids   *Eubacterium*

Table 3-5 Recent taxonomic changes

New Nomenclature	Prior Nomenclature	References
Bacteroides asaccharolyticus	*B. melaninogenicus* subsp. *asaccharolyticus* (in part)	32,170
B. buccae	*B. ruminicola* - human strains (in part)	70
B. buccalis	*B. oralis* (in part)	173
B. corporis	*B. melaninogenicus* subsp. *intermedius* (in part)	80
B. denticola	New species	71
B. endodontalis	New species	169
B. gingivalis	*B. melaninogenicus* subsp. *asaccharolyticus* (in part)	32,170
B. gracilis	*B. ureolyticus* (in part)	166
B. intermedius	*B. melaninogenicus* subsp. *intermedius* (in part)	80
B. levii	*B. melaninogenicus* subsp. *levii*	80
B. loescheii	New species	71
B. macacae	New species	32,142
B. melaninogenicus	*B. melaninogenicus* subsp. *melaninogenicus* (in part)	71
B. oris	*B. ruminicola* - human strains (in part)	70
B. veroralis	*B. oralis* (in part)	173
B. zoogleoformans	Reinstated	70,73
Capnocytophaga *	New genus (includes *B. ochraceous*)	70
Clostridium barati	Includes *C. perenne* and *C. paraperfringens*	70
C. bullosum	*F. bullosum*	70
C. symbiosum	*F. symbiosum*	70
Eubacterium plauti	*F. plauti*	70
Fusobacterium periodonticum	New species	143
Peptostreptococcus asaccharolyticus	*Peptococcus asaccharolyticus*	44
P. indolicus	*Peptococcus indolicus*	44
P. magnus	*Peptococcus magnus*	44
P. prevotii	*Peptococcus prevotii*	44
P. tetradius	New species	44
Staphylococcus saccharolyticus	*Peptococcus saccharolyticus*	
Streptococcus parvulus	*Peptostreptococcus parvulus*	26
Veillonella sp.	Includes *V. alcalescens, atypica, dispar* and *parvula*	107
Wolinella recta	New species	166
W. succinogenes	New species (basonym *V. succinogenes*)	166

* not an obligate anaerobe

Anaerobe Laboratory Manual or *Bergey's Manual of Determinative Bacteriology* to identify the isolate. Thioglycolate-based media with bromthymol blue indicator give similar results (34). Results obtained in other systems may not agree with these tables. Gas chromatographic analysis may be performed on any carbohydrate-containing medium that supports good growth or the organism. (See chapter 4 for procedures and discussion.)

Flow diagrams for the identification of anaerobic gram-negative bacilli, black-pigmented *Bacteroides* sp., and anaerobic cocci are shown in Figures 3-7, 3-8, and 3-9.

Gram-negative bacilli. Only *Bacteroides*, *Fusobacterium*, and *Wolinella* are encountered in most clinical specimens. Other gram-negative bacilli, such as *Leptotrichia*, *Desulfomonas*, *Butyrivibrio*, *Succinivibrio*, *Succinimonas*, *Anaerovibrio*, *Anaerobiospirillum*, *Mobiluncus,* and *Selenomonas,* are rarely present in clinical specimens. They may occur as "contaminating" normal flora or as causes of infection. Bacteremia in an immunocompromised host is the most common form of infection. Initial differentiation of these genera is based on motility, flagellar arrangement, cellular morphology, and end-products of metabolism (Table 3-4) (25,73). All gram-negative bacilli that are curved or metabolically fastidious or that form spreading or pitting colonies should be checked for motility. If not identified as a *Wolinella* sp., they should be identified according to Table 3-4. Large fusiform bacilli may be *Leptotrichia,* and the characteristic GLC pattern should be confirmed.

Colonies of the *B. fragilis* group on BA are 2 to 3 mm in diameter, circular, entire, convex, and grey to white. Hemin enhances growth of most strains. The cells can be uniform or pleomorphic (some with vacuoles); this is medium and age-dependent. Good growth in 20% bile (2% Oxgall) is characteristic of the *B. fragilis* group, except for *B. uniformis*. Some non-*B. fragilis* group organisms are bile resistant; however, *B. splanchnicus* and *B. eggerthii* are sucrose negative. Table 3-6 is a key for speciating the bile resistant *Bacteroides*. *B. thetaiotaomicron* and *B. ovatus* may be difficult to differentiate; xylan and salicin are useful in separating these two species (137). In addition, *B. ovatus* has a more ovoid shape on Gram stain than *B. thetaiotaomicron*. The unnamed *B. fragilis* DNA homology group 3452A closely resembles *B. distasonis*. 3452A is arabinose-positive and catalase negative, whereas *B. distasonis* is usually catalase positive and arabinose negative (79). Bile resistant organisms that do not fit any of the described species listed may be designated as " *B. fragilis* group".

The bile sensitive non-pigmented *Bacteroides* form three major subgroups: 1) saccharolytic, 2) saccharolytic and strongly proteolytic, and 3) asaccharolytic. Table 3-7 lists the more important or more commonly encountered species in this group.

The saccharolytic *Bacteroides* are subdivided into two categories: pentose fermenters or non-fermenters (arabinose and xylose usually tested). *B. oris* and *B. buccae* (formerly *B. ruminicola*) are pentose fermenters. They are phenotypically very similar but can be differentiated by the beta-glucosidase test. *B. oris* strains

Table 3-6 Characteristics of bile resistant *Bacteroides* species

	Growth in 20% bile	Indole production	Catalase	Esculin hydrolysis	Fermentation of							Fatty acids from PYG
					Sucrose	Maltose	Rhamnose	Salicin	Trehalose	Arabinose	Xylan	
B. fragilis group												
B. distasonis	+	−	$+^-$	+	+		V	+	+	$-^+$		A p S (pa) (ib iv l)
3452A homology group	+	−	−	+	+		$+^-$	$+^-$	+	+		
B. fragilis	+	−	+	+	+		−	−	−	−		A p S, pa
B. vulgatus	+	−	$-^+$	$-^+$	+		+	−	−	+		A p S
B. ovatus	+	+	$-^+$	+	+		+	+	+	+	+	A p S pa (ib iv l)
B. thetaiotaomicron	+	+	$+^-$	+	+		+	$-^+$	+	+	−	A p S pa
B. uniformis	W^+	+	$-^+$	+	+		$-^+$	$+^-$	−	+		a p l S (ib iv)
Other												
B. eggerthii	+	+	−	+	−	+	$+^-$	−	−		+	A p S (ib iv l)
B. splanchnicus	W^+	+	−	+	−	−	−	−	−	−	+	A P ib b iv S (l)

are usually more resistant to penicillin (2 U/ml) than *B. buccae. B. zoogleoformans* is an oral bacterium that may ferment pentoses; it is isolated infrequently from clinical specimens. This organism forms a highly viscous, tenacious (zoogleal) mass in broth culture. Salicin and xylan are useful in differentiating *B. oralis, B. buccalis,* and *B. veroralis* (formerly *B. oralis*) (173). Certain strains of the *B. melaninogenicus* group require more than 21 days to develop pigment, and these strains, especially *B. loescheii*, closely resemble the *B. oralis* group. The gelatin reaction may aid in separating these organisms; *B. loescheii, B. melaninogenicus,* and *B. denticola* are usually gelatin positive, whereas *B. oralis, B. buccalis,* and *B. veroralis* are gelatin negative (71,173).

　　B. bivius and *B. disiens* are both saccharolytic and strongly proteolytic. Gelatin and milk are usually digested within 2 to 3 days (although milk may take longer). Lactose is the key differentiating sugar: *B. bivius* is positive and *B. disiens* is negative. Their colonies may fluoresce a light orange to pink (coral) under UV light and should not be confused with the brick red fluorescence of the pigmenting *Bacteroides* sp. *B. bivius* and *B. disiens* are phenotypically similar to *B. intermedius* and *B. corporis*. Indole production and sucrose and lactose

Table 3-7 Characteristics of non-pigmented bile sensitive *Bacteroides* species

	Fermentation of							Esculin hydrolysis	Beta-glucosidase	Zoogleal mass	Indole production	Gelatin hydrolysis	Fatty acids from PYG
	Glucose	Sucrose	Lactose	Arabinose	Xylose	Salicin	Xylan						
Saccharolytic													
Pentose fermenters													
B. oris	+	+	+	+	+	+		+			−		A S (p ib iv)
B. buccae	+	+	+	+	+	+		+	+		−		A S (p ib b iv l)
B. zoogleoformans	+	+	+	V	V	V		+	−	+	+⁻		A P S (ib iv)
Pentose non-fermenters													
B. oralis	+	+	+	−	−	+		+			−		A S (l)
B. buccalis	+	+	+	−	−	−	−	+			−		a iv S
B. veroralis	+	+	+	−	−	−	+	+			−		a S
Saccharolytic and proteolytic													
B. bivius†	+	−	+	−	−	−		−			−	+	A iv S (ib)
B. disiens	+	−	−	−	−	−		−			−	+	A S (p ib iv)
Non-saccharolytic or weakly saccharolytic													
B. capillosus	W⁻	−	−	−	−	−		+			−	−	a s (p l)
B. praeacutus	−	−	−	−	−	−		−			+	+	A p ib B IV a (l)
B. puredinis	−	−	−	−	−	−		−			+	+	a P ib b IV S (l)

† Most strains are black pigmented on laked rabbit blood agar after prolonged incubation; see text for differential characteristics that separate *B. bivius* from the other pigmented *Bacteroides*.

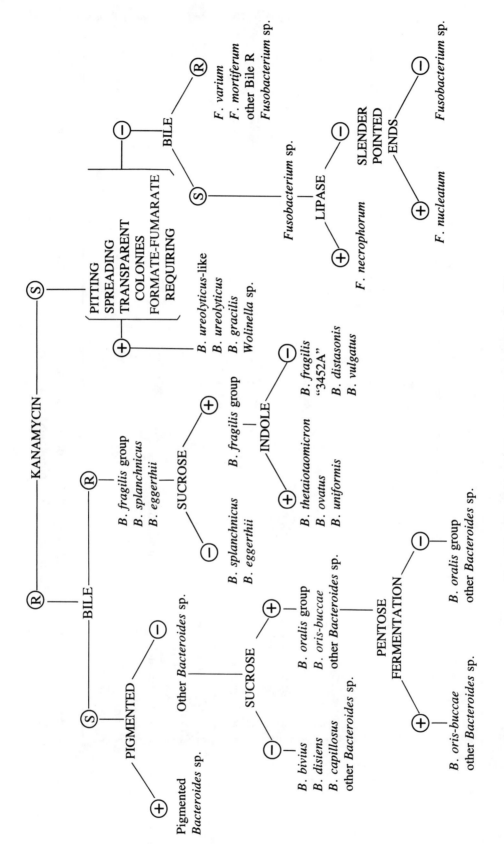

Fig. 3-7. Flow chart for anaerobic gram negative bacilli

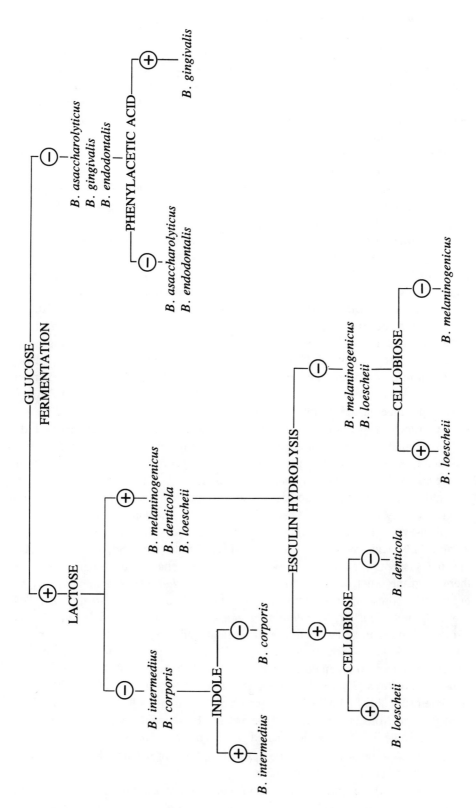

Fig. 3-8. Flow chart for black pigmented *Bacteroides* species

fermentation, plus pigment production on laked rabbit blood agar, are useful characteristics for differentiation. *B. intermedius* is indole positive and usually sucrose positive; the other three are indole and sucrose negative. *B. bivius* is lactose positive; the others are lactose negative. *B. corporis* produces pigment fairly rapidly; *B. disiens* does not produce pigment even after prolonged incubation on laked rabbit blood. It has been reported recently that *B. bivius* produces pigment on laked rabbit blood agar after prolonged incubation (personal communication, K. Ueno and H. Shah).

Asaccharolytic, non-pigmented, bile sensitive *Bacteroides* sp. are infrequently isolated from clinical specimens. *B. capillosus* may ferment glucose weakly, is esculin positive, coagulates milk, and may grow better with Tween 80-supplemented media. *B. praeacutus* and *B. putredinis* are asaccharolytic and proteolytic; an indole test will differentiate them. *B. pneumosintes* is a tiny bacillus (<0.3 μm) and forms barely visible colonies. Negative staining may be required to see cells, and magnification may be needed to visualize colonies.

The pigmented *Bacteroides* species vary greatly in the degree and rapidity of pigmentation, depending primarily on the type of blood used; laked rabbit blood is the most reliable (73). Two to 21 days may be required to detect pigmentation, which ranges from buff to tan to black. A few strains may not form pigment within 21 days and their identity must be established by other biochemical tests. *A. odontolyticus* may be confused initially with these organisms, since it usually produces a red pigment. A Gram stain will differentiate them. The pigmented *Bacteroides* fluoresce pink, orange, chartreuse, or brick red. Brick red is the only reliable color for presumptive identification if pigment has not yet been produced, since some non-pigmented *Bacteroides* fluoresce coral or pink. Fluorescence is masked by pigment production.

Table 3-8 is a key for speciating the pigmented *Bacteroides*. Several new species have been described (Table 3-5). *B. asaccharolyticus* and *B. gingivalis* are phenotypically very similar. The production of phenylacetic acid, a non-volatile fatty acid, by *B. gingivalis* will differentiate them (84, 105, 106). Their unusual susceptibility to vancomycin and non-saccharolytic properties separate them from the other pigmented *Bacteroides*. *B. endodontalis*, a newly described organism, is presently phenotypically indistinguishable from *B. asaccharolyticus* (169). As noted earlier, *B. melaninogenicus*, *B. loescheii*, and *B. denticola* may require 21 days in order to develop pigment and may, therefore, be confused with *B. oralis*, *B. veroralis*, or *B. buccalis*. *B. macacae* is an indole positive, catalase positive, pigmented *Bacteroides* that has been isolated from the gingivae of monkeys (32), and we have isolated one strain from a dog bite wound specimen (unpublished data). *B. levii*, which is similar to *B. corporis*, has rarely been isolated from human clinical specimens. Pigmented *Bacteroides* not classifiable by Table 3-8 may be designated as "pigmented *Bacteroides* sp.".

Bacteroides species is the name applied to those organisms that do not fit the species described in Tables 3-6 to 3-8.

Fusobacterium sp. are resistant to vancomycin, susceptible to kanamycin and colistin, and produce butyric acid without isobutyric or isovaleric acids. The

Table 3-8 Characteristics of pigmented *Bacteroides* species †

	Indole production	Lipase	Fermentation of			Esculin hydrolysis	Phenylacetic acid production	Fatty acids from PYG
			Glucose	Lactose	Cellobiose			
B. asaccharolyticus	+	−	−	−	−		−	A p ib B iv S
B. gingivalis	+	−	−	−	−		+	a p ib B IV s pa
B. intermedius	+	+	+	−	−			A iv S (p ib)
B. corporis	−	−	+	−	−			A ib iv S (b)
B. melaninogenicus	−	−	+	+	−	−		A S (ib iv l)
B. denticola	−	−	+	+	−	+		A S (ib iv l)
B. loescheii	−	−⁺	+	+	+	V		a S (l)

† *B. endodontalis*, a newly described pigmented *Bacteroides*, is phenotypically indistinguisable from *B. asaccharolyticus*.
B. bivius forms black pigmented colonies on laked rabbit blood agar after prolonged incubation. See Table 3-7 for further characteristics and the text for differentiation from other pigmented *Bacteroides* sp.

fusobacteria are weakly saccharolytic or non-fermentative. Most are non-proteolytic (gelatin negative). Colonial morphology varies greatly. In addition, many strains fluoresce chartreuse under UV light and others produce greening of the agar. The most common clinical isolates, *F. nucleatum* and *F. necrophorum*, are indole positive. These two organisms are discussed in the Level II speciation.

Table 3-9 characterizes the more commonly isolated fusobacteria. Conversion of threonine (Th) and lactate (Lt) to propionic acid is important in speciating some of them. Bizarre pleomorphic bacilli with very large coccoid forms (round bodies) are characteristic of *F. mortiferum*. This organism may grow poorly on BBE agar and turn the agar black. *F. periodonticum* is a newly described species (based on three oral isolates from one individual) that is indole positive, bile sensitive, ferments glucose, fructose, and galactose, and converts Th, but not Lt, to propionic acid (143). *Fusobacterium* sp. is the name given to those organisms that do not fit the species described in Table 3-9.

Gram-negative cocci. Veillonella, Acidaminococcus, and *Megasphaera* comprise the genera of anaerobic gram-negative cocci. *Veillonella* species are part of the normal mouth, upper respiratory, and gastrointestinal tract flora; *Megasphaera* and *Acidaminococcus* are part of the intestinal flora. *Veillonella* is isolated more frequently from clinical specimens than are *Megasphaera* and *Acidaminococcus*. Table 3-10 is a key for differentiating these three genera.

Table 3-9 Characteristics of *Fusobacterium* species

	Distinctive cellular morphology	Indole production	Growth in 20% bile	Lipase	Gas in glucose agar	Fermentation of			Esculin hydrolysis	Lactate converted to propionate	Threonine converted to propionate	Fatty acids from PYG
						Glucose	Fructose	Mannose				
F. nucleatum	slender pointed ends	+	−	−	$-^2$	$-^w$	$-^w$	−	−	−	+	a p B (L s)
F. gonidiaformans	gonidia forms	+	−	−	4^2	−	−	−	−	−	+	A p B (l s)
F. necrophorum	none*	+	$-^+$	$+^-$	4^2	$-^w$	$-^w$	−	−	+	+	a p B (l s)
F. naviforme	boat shape	+	−	−	−	w^-	$-^w$	−	−	−	−	a B L (p s)
F. varium	none	$+^-$	+	−	4	w^+	w^+	w^+	−	−	+	a p B L (s)
F. mortiferum	bizarre, round bodies	−	+	−	4	$+^w$	$+^w$	$+^w$	+	−	+	a p B (v l a)
F. russii	none	−	−	−	2^-	−	−	−	−	−	−	a B L

* May have same microscopic morphology as *F. mortiferum*

Table 3-10 Characteristics of anaerobic gram-negative cocci

	Nitrate reduction	Catalase	Glucose	Fatty acids from PYG
Veillonella sp.	+	V	−	A p
Acidaminococcus fermentans	−	−	−	A B
Megasphaera elsdenii	−	−	+	a ib b iv v C

Gram-positive cocci. The anaerobic gram-positive cocci are part of the normal flora of the mouth, skin, upper respiratory tract, and large intestine. They are isolated with high frequency from all sources of specimens except for blood, central nervous system, and animal bite wounds (Table 1-3). *Peptostreptococcus* and *Streptococcus* are the two genera of clinical importance. *Peptostreptococcus magnus* is the most frequently isolated coccus in this and other laboratories (21). *Ruminococcus* and *Coprococcus*, members of the normal fecal flora, and *Peptococcus niger* and *P. indolicus* are rarely isolated from clinical specimens (25,72). Recent taxonomic changes have transferred all the *Peptococcus* sp., except *P. niger*, to the genus *Peptostreptococcus*; *P. saccharolyticus* to the genus *Staphylococcus*, and *P. parvulus* to the *Streptococcus* genus (Table 3-5). *P. tetradius* is the new designation for " *Gaffkya anaerobia*". Table 3-11 lists differential characteristics for the gram-positive cocci.

Gas-liquid chromatography and biochemical tests are needed for genus level identification and speciation of most anaerobic gram-positive cocci except for *P. anaerobius* (SPS susceptible) and *P. asaccharolyticus* (indole positive). The butyric acid producers *P. tetradius* and *P. prevotii* are very similar, except that *P. tetradius* is strongly saccharolytic and urease positive, whereas *P. prevotii* is weakly saccharolytic (pH 5.7 to 5.9) and is usually urease-negative. *P. anaerobius* is the only coccus that produces isocaproic acid. *P. magnus* and *P. micros* are differentiated primarily by cell size: *P. magnus* cells are ≥ 0.6 μm and *P. micros* <0.6 μm in diameter. *P. micros* usually forms short chains and its colonies are small, white, and sometimes have a halo of discoloration surrounding them.

The anaerobic streptococci (*S. intermedius*, *S. constellatus*, and *S. morbillorum*) are strongly saccharolytic and produce lactic acid as the sole major end-product. Cellular morphology varies in size and form (chains and pairs). Unlike true anaerobes, these organisms are resistant to metronidazole and may become aerotolerant after subculturing.

Organisms that do not fit the described species are designated as anaerobic *Streptococcus* sp. or *Peptostreptococcus* sp.

Gram-positive sporeforming bacilli. *Clostridium* sp. form a heterogeneous group of sporeforming gram-positive bacilli. They are widely distributed in the environment and constitute part of the normal human intestinal flora. Most

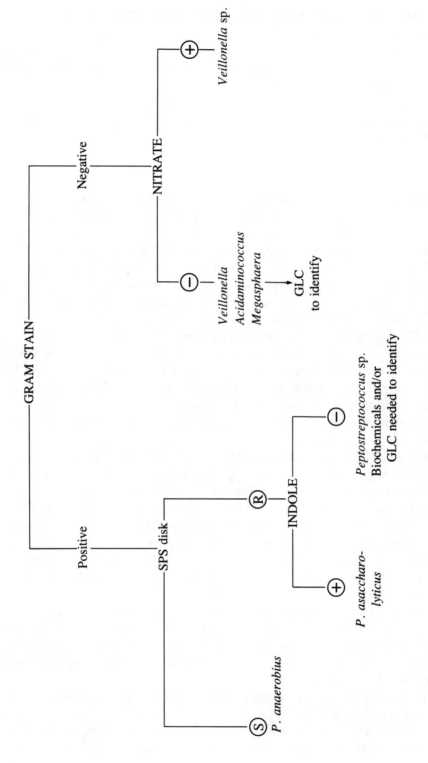

Fig. 3-9. Flow chart for anaerobic cocci

Table 3-11 Characteristics of anaerobic gram-positive cocci

	Indole production	Butyric acid production	Isocaproic acid production	Lactic acid only major end-product	Fermentation of Glucose	Cellobiose	Lactose	Maltose	Sucrose	Urease	Cell size ≥0.6 µm	Fatty acids from PYG
Peptostreptococcus asaccharolyticus	+	+	−	−	−	−	−	−	−	−		B (A l p)
P. prevotii	−	+	−	−	−ʷ	−	−	wˉ	wˉ	−⁺		B (A L p)
P. tetradius	−	+	−	−	+	−	−	+	+	+		B L (a p)
P. anaerobius	−	v	+	−	wˉ	−	−	wˉ	wˉ	−		A IC (ib b iv)
P. productus	−	−	−	−	+	+	+	+	+	−		A l s
P. micros	−	−	−	−	−	−	−	−	−	−	−	A (s)
P. magnus	−	−	−	−	−	−	−	−	−	−	+	A
Streptococcus sp.	−	−	−	+	+	V	V	+	+			L (a)

infections are endogenous, although a few noteworthy exogenous intoxications such as food poisoning *(C. perfringens)*, botulism *(C. botulinum)* and tetanus *(C. tetani)* occur.

In addition to the Nagler positive group (Table 3-12), the *Clostridium* sp. may be subdivided into three groups based on proteolytic (gelatin hydrolysis) and saccharolytic (glucose fermentation) properties (Table 3-13). The organisms listed in Tables 3-12 and 3-13 represent the more commonly isolated or pathogenic clostridia. A number are relatively resistant to antibiotics. There are numerous other species not listed, and these may be identified using *Bergey's Manual* or the *VPI Anaerobe Laboratory Manual* and current literature (25,69,73).

Certain factors must be considered when identifying *Clostridium* sp. First, it is important to note that some of the clostridia stain gram-negative; however, the special potency antibiotic disk pattern (colistin resistant and vancomycin sensitive) will demonstrate the gram-positivity of the isolate. Second, the spores of some species are rarely detected microscopically, so that an ethanol or heat spore test may be necessary. Third, the colony morphology is often pleomorphic, so it appears that the culture is mixed. Subcultures of single colonies yield the same pleomorphic types. Fourth, the aerotolerant clostridia may be confused with *Bacillus* sp. *Clostridium* species sporulate anaerobically only, grow much better anaerobically (larger colonies), and are almost always catalase negative, whereas *Bacillus* sp. sporulate aerobically only, usually grow better aerobically, and are usually catalase positive.

Three of the Nagler positive clostridia are discussed in the Level II speciation section and are summarized in Table 3-12. The rare urease negative strains of *C.*

Table 3-12 Characteristics of Nagler positive *Clostridium* species

	Indole production	Gelatin hydrolysis	Urease	Growth enhanced by 1% mannose	Phenylacetic acid produced	Glutamic acid decarboxylase
C. perfringens	−	+	−			
C. barati	−	−	−			
C. bifermentans	+	+	−	−	−	−*
C. sordellii	+	+	+⁻	+	V	+

* Only a few strains have been tested

sordellii are difficult to differentiate from *C. bifermentans*. *C. bifermentans* does not produce phenylacetic acid (PAA), its growth is enhanced by 1% mannose, and it is glutamic acid decarboxylase negative; whereas *C. sordellii* may produce PAA, its growth is not enhanced by 1% mannose, and it is glutamic acid decarboxylase positive (only a few strains have been tested) (78).

C. novyi type A is lecithinase and lipase positive and may swarm. It is infrequently isolated. Types B, C, and D vary in these properties and are unlikely to be isolated from human clinical material. *C. sporogenes* is lipase positive, swarms, and has colonies that firmly adhere to the agar. It is phenotypically the same as *C. botulinum* types A, B, and F. Toxin neutralization in mice, polyacrylamide gel electrophoresis (PAGE) of soluble cellular proteins, or GLC of trimethylsilyl derivatives of whole cell hydrolysates are necessary for differentiating *C. sporogenes* and *C. botulinum*. The different *C. botulinum* types vary in saccharolytic, proteolytic, and lipase activity. Suspected *C. botulinum* isolates or possible *C. botulinum*-containing material (e.g., suspected food in food poisoning cases) should be referred to the local or state public health laboratories. The swarmer *C. septicum* produces a medusa head-like colony in 4 to 6 hours that becomes a heavy film of growth that covers the plate by 24 to 48 hours. The isolation of *C. difficile* from stool samples of patients with suspected antimicrobial-associated diarrhea or pseudomembranous colitis is discussed later in this chapter. This organism produces a characteristic horse-stable odor, fluoresces chartreuse, forms pleomorphic colonies, and produces a characteristic yellow ground-glass colony on cycloserine cefoxitin fructose agar (CCFA) (54).

C. ramosum is a thin gram-variable rod that has a small round or oval terminal spore, when present. It is one of the *Clostridium* sp. resistant to clindamycin. *C. clostridiiforme* stains gram-negative and forms characteristic elongated football-shaped cells that rarely show spores. It may be misidentified initially as

Table 3-13 Characteristics of gram-positive sporeforming bacilli †

	Gelatin hydrolysis	Glucose fermentation	Lecithinase	Lipase	Indole	Butyric acid produced in PYG	Isoacids produced in PYG	Aerobic growth	Urease	Milk reaction	Fermentation of — Lactose	Maltose	Fructose	Cellobiose	Arabinose	Mannose	Xylose	Nitrate reduction	Spore location	End products from PYG
Saccharolytic proteolytic																				
C. bifermentans	+	+	+	–	+	(+)	(+)	–	–	d	–	W⁻	V	–	–	–ᵂ	–	–	OS	A (p ib b iv ic l s)
C. sordellii	+	+	+	–	+	(+)	(+)	–	+⁻	d	–	W⁺	V	–	–	–ᵂ	–	–	OS	A (p ib b iv ic l)
C. perfringens	+	+	+	–	–	+	–	–	–	dᶜ	+	+	+	+⁻	–	+	–	+⁻	–	A B L (ps)
C. novyi type A	+	+	+	+	–	+	+	–	–	c	–	V⁻	–ᵂ	–	–	–	–	–	OS	A P B
C. sporogenes	+	+	–	+	+	+	+	–	–	d	–	–ᵂ	–ᵂ	–	–	–ᵂ	–	–	OS	A B ib iv (p v ic l s)
C. cadaveris	+	+	–	–	–	+	–	–	–	cd	+	+	V	–	–	+	–	–	OT	A B (l s)
C. septicum	+	+	–	–	–	+	–	–	–	cd	+	+	+	+ᵂ	–	+	–	–	OS	A B (p l)
C. difficile	+	+	–	–	–	+	+	–	–	–	+	–	+	+ᵂ	–	+⁻	–ᵂ	V	OS	A ib B iv ic (v l)
C. putrificum	+	+	–	–	–⁺	+	+	–	–	d	–	–ᵂ	–ᵂ	–	–	–	–	–	OS	A ib B iv (p v ic l s)
Saccharolytic non-proteolytic																				
C. barati	–	+	+	–	–	+	–	–	–	c	+ᵂ	+ᵂ	+	+	–	+	–	V	OT	A B L (s)
C. tertium	–	+	–	–	–	+	–	+	–	c	+	+	+	+	–	+	+⁻	+⁻	OS	A B L (s)
C. butyricum	–	+	–	–	–	+	–	–	–	c	+	+	+	+	–	+	+	–	OS	A B F (l s)
C. innocuum	–	+	–	–	–	–	–	–	–	–	–	–	+	+	+⁻	+	–ᵂ	–	OT	a B L (s)
C. ramosum	–	+	–	–	–	–	–	–	–	c	+⁻	+ᵂ	+	+⁻	V	+ᵂ	–ᵂ	–ᵂ	R/OT	A L (s)
C. clostridiiforme	–	+	–	–	–	–	–	–	–	c	+⁻	+ᵂ	+	+	V	+	+	+⁻	OS	A (l s)
Asaccharolytic proteolytic																				
C. tetani	+	–	–	–	V	+	–	–	–	d⁻	–	–	–	–	–	–	–	–	RT	A P B (p l s)
C. hastiforme	+	–	+⁻	–	–	+	+	–	–	–ᵈ	–	–	–	–	–	–	–	+	S	A B iv ib (p ic)
C. subterminale	+	–	–	–	–	+	+	+⁻	–	dᶜ	–	–	–	–	–	–	–	–	OS	A B ib IV (p ic l s)
C. histolyticum	+	–	–	–	–	–	–	+⁻	–	d	–	–	–	–	–	–	–	–	OS	A (l s)
C. limosum	+	–	+	–	–	–	–	–	–	d	–	–	–	–	–	–	–	–	S	A (l s)

† *C. botulinum* types vary in proteolytic, saccharolytic, and lipase reactions. Send suspected isolates or suspected *C. botulinum* containing material to the appropriate local or state agency.

a *Bacteroides* sp. or *Fusobacterium* sp. *C. oroticum* has a similar cell shape, but it often has spores and forms chains as seen on the Gram stain smear.

C. tetani may form a thin film of growth over the entire plate, especially on moist media. This characteristically drumstick-shaped gram-positive bacillus is rarely isolated from clinical material of patients with tetanus.

Gram-positive nonsporeforming bacilli. The nonsporeforming gram-positive bacilli consist of several genera that are differentiated from each other by their metabolic end-products as described in Table 3-4. (See Chapter 4 for methods and discussion.) These bacteria form part of the normal human flora at most sites (Table 1-1) but occur infrequently in infections. *Actinomyces* and *Arachnia* are the major agents in actinomycosis. *B. eriksonii* has been responsible for a few serious pulmonary infections. *Propionibacterium* sp. are involved occasionally in infections (usually endocarditis and infections with implanted devices such as ventriculo-atrial shunts or artificial hip joints). Speciation of most of the gram-positive nonsporeforming bacilli is beyond the scope of this manual and clinical need, except for *Actinomyces* and certain other rare species.

Table 3-14 lists characteristics used in identifying the more commonly isolated or clinically important bacteria in this group. Several generalizations can be made using results from the nitrate, catalase, and indole reactions: 1) a catalase positive organism is probably a *Propionibacterium* sp. or *A. viscosus*; 2) a nitrate positive organism is probably not a *Bifidobacterium* or *Lactobacillus* sp; and 3) an indole positive organism is probably a *Propionibacterium*. In addition, many strains of *Actinomyces* and *Propionibacterium* and some strains of *Bifidobacterium* and *Lactobacillus* are microaerophilic, although they grow best anaerobically.

Most *Actinomyces* are microaerophilic (CO_2 is required for maximum growth) and are slow growers, requiring more than 48 hours incubation for growth to appear on primary culture. Branching, beading and diphtheroid-shaped gram-positive bacilli are seen on the Gram stain smear. *A. israelii* is noted for its molar tooth colony; however, its colonies may also be smooth. Although it is reported that the red pigment production of *A. odontolyticus* is enhanced by exposure to air, these red colonies are also isolated from the anaerobically incubated BA plate. *A. naeslundii* forms a tan pigmented colony after prolonged incubation. *A. viscosus* is the only catalase positive *Actinomyces*. *A. meyeri* is a small bacillus and is the only strict anaerobe in this genus.

Propionibacterium are pleomorphic bacilli that may appear to branch. *P. acnes* is the most commonly isolated species and is often a contaminant in blood cultures. *Bifidobacterium* sp. with bifurcated ends may also appear to be branching; however, these bacilli are generally larger in diameter than *Actinomyces* or *Propionibacterium*. Lactobacilli have straight sides and may occur in chains. The *Eubacterium* genus is comprised of those gram-positive nonsporeforming bacilli that have a GLC pattern not characteristic of the other genera. *E. lentum* is the most commonly isolated species. Its features are described in the Level II speciation section.

Table 3-14 Level III identification of gram-positive nonsporeforming bacilli.

	Nitrate reduction	Catalase	Indole production	Esculin hydrolysis	Urease	Red colony	Oxygen tolerance	Fermentation of							Fatty acids from PYG
								Glucose	Mannitol	Raffinose	Ribose	Trehalose	Erythritol	Maltose	
Actinomyces sp.	+	$-^+$	−	$+^-$	V			+							A S (L)
A. israelii	$+^-$	−	−	+	−		AM	+	+	$+^-$	$+^-$	$+^-$		+	A L S
A. odontolyticus	+	−	−	$+^-$	−	$+^-$	AM	+	−	−	$-^w$	−		V	A S
A. naeslundii	$+^-$	+	−	$+^-$	+		MF	+	−	+	V	$+^-$		+	A L S
A. viscosus	$+^-$	−	−	V	+		AM	+	−	+	$-^+$	V		+	A L S
A. meyeri	$-^+$	−	−	$-^+$	−		A	+	−	−	$+^w$	−		+	A S
Propionibacterium sp.	V	V	$-^+$	V			AM	+							A P
P. acnes	$+^-$	$+^-$	$+^-$	−			AM	+					$-^+$	−	A p (iv L s)
P. granulosum	−	+	−	−									−	$+^-$	A p (iv s)
P. avidum	−	+	−	+				+					$+^w$	+	A p (iv s)
Bifidobacterium sp.	−	−	−	$+^-$			AM	+	+	+	+	+	−		A L [A > L]
B. eriksonii	−	−	−	+			A	+	+	+	+	+		+	A L [A > L]
Lactobacillus sp.	$-^+$	−	−	V			AM	$+^-$							L (a) [L > a]
Eubacterium sp.	V	−	$-^+$	$+^-$			A	$+^-$					−	−	
E. lentum	+	$-^+$	−	−			A	−					−	−	(a l s)

Level III identification systems. Several identification systems are currently available, including macrotube and microtube, agar plate, and enzyme substrate types. The PRAS system (macrotube) is still the standard method.

PRAS biochemicals are inoculated by either the open or closed technique. The open technique utilizes a special apparatus that allows for a continuous flow of anaerobic gas into the tube during manipulations, whereas the closed technique utilizes a needle and syringe to inject the inoculum into the tube through a rubber stopper. This latter system has been further modified by Scott Laboratories by replacing the rubber stopper with a Hungate type screw cap (PRAS II). Scott Laboratories has also developed several computer programs to aid in identification of the isolate at various levels of identification (18).

Five to ten drops of a young broth culture (6 to 72 hours, depending upon rapidity of growth) are inoculated into each tube of the appropriate test medium (Table 3-15). One to two drops are plated onto a BA plate (incubate anaerobically) to determine the purity and viability of the broth culture. The tubes are incubated at 35C and read as soon as they show good growth or 1 day after there

Table 3-15 Level III PRAS tests for identification of anaerobic isolates

B. fragilis group	Pigmented *Bacteroides* sp.	Gram-negative bacillus	*Fuso-bacterium*	Gram-negative coccus
PY	PY	PY	GNB scheme	PY
PYG	PYG	PYG	TH	PYG
ARAB	CB	ARAB	LT	PYR
CB	ES	CB	PYG AGAR DEEP	INO$_3$
ES	FRUC	ES		
RH	LAC	LAC		
RI	ML	ML		
SAL	SUC	MANNOSE		
SUC	GEL	MEB		
TRE	INO$_3$	RAF		
BILE		RH		
INO$_3$		SAL		
XYLAN (if indole positive)		ST		
		SUC		
		TRE		
		XYL		
		GEL		
		MILK		
		INO$_3$		
		BILE		

Table 3-15 Level III PRAS tests for identification of anaerobic isolates (cont.)

Gram-positive coccus	Gram-positive nonsporeforming bacillus	*Clostridium*	*C. difficile*	*Actinomyces-Propionibacterium*
PY	Use all the	PY	PYG	PY
PYG	biochemicals	PYG	ES	PYG
CB	listed and	ES	FRUC	ARAB
ES	additional	FRUC	ML	ES
LAC	tests listed	LAC	MANNOSE	FRUC
ML	in quality	ML	XYL	INT
MANNOSE	control sec-	MANT	INO₃	LAC
SUC	tion	MANNOSE		ML
TW		MELZ		MANT
INO₃		MEB		RAF
		RI		RI
Indole positive		SAL		SORB
gram-positive coccus		SUC		ST
PY		XYL		TRE
PYG		GEL		GEL
INO₃		MILK		TW
LT		TW		INO₃
		INO₃		UREA

ABBREVIATIONS

PY	Peptone yeast	MELZ	PY-melezitose
PYG	PY-glucose	MILK	Milk
ARAB	PY-arabinose	PYR	Pyruvate
BILE	PYG-bile	RAF	PY-raffinose
CB	PY-cellobiose	RH	PY-rhamnose
ES	PY-esculin	RI	PY-ribose
GEL	Gelatin	SAL	PY-salicin
FRUC	PY-fructose	SORB	PY-sorbitol
INT	PY-inositol	SUC	PY-sucrose
INO₃	Indole-nitrate	ST	Starch
LT	PY-lactate	TH	PY-threonine
LAC	PY-lactose	TRE	PY-trehalose
ML	PY-maltose	TW	PYG-tween
MANT	PY-mannitol	UREA	Urea
MANNOSE	PY-mannose	XYLAN	PY-xylan
MEB	PY-melibiose	XYL	PY-xylose

is no increase in turbidity. Growth is graded 1+ to 4+ after the tubes have been inverted several times to ensure resuspension of organisms that may have settled to the bottom. The pH is recorded for all carbohydrate, esculin, milk, and starch media. Esculin, gelatin, and starch hydrolysis, indole production, nitrate reduction and growth in bile are determined. The milk tube is checked for clotting and digestion. Appropriate biochemicals are processed for GLC.

The PRAS system is expensive, labor-intensive, and not problem-free. The major problem is interpretation of biochemical results. The following three points may aid in reducing potential errors:

1) The inoculum must be a young culture of at least 2+ turbidity. An old culture contains predominantly non-viable organisms and its use may lead to unreliable results. Since some anaerobes grow poorly in thioglycolate or peptone-yeast broth, the addition of supplements may be necessary to enhance growth. If growth in the thioglycolate broth culture is less than 2+, then perform growth stimulation tests (see Appendix) and add 5 to 10 drops of the appropriate supplement to each PRAS tube. Tween-80 can be added directly to the inoculum broth.

2) The anaerobe tested must be in pure culture and viable. Do not read biochemicals of mixed cultures; reisolate the organism and repeat the biochemical inoculation. If the isolate fails to grow on the purity and viability plate and there is no visible turbidity in the tubes, biochemicals cannot be read and must be repeated after determining the growth requirements of the isolate. If the isolate fails to grow on the plate, but there appears to be turbidity in the biochemical tubes, then subculture the PYG to determine that the turbidity is growth of the isolate and not merely inoculum or a contaminant. If the organism grows on the plate, but not in the biochemical tubes after 2 to 3 days of incubation, then perform growth stimulation tests and reinoculate. Do not incubate non-turbid biochemicals for >5 days, as growth rarely occurs beyond that time.

3) Some anaerobes characteristically grow with heavy turbidity while others do not, and any inconsistencies in growth throughout the series of tubes should be investigated. Unusually heavy growth in one or two tubes suggests either the presence of a growth factor or contamination. Gram stain or subculture an aliquot of material from the questionable tubes to rule out contamination. Poor or no growth in one or two tubes of a series showing good growth may be due to an oxidized tube (pink color due to resazurin indicator change) or a tube skipped during inoculation. *P. acnes* and *Staphylococcus* sp. are the usual contaminants. If the indole and nitrate tests are both positive, then suspect that *P. acnes* is present in the tubes. An aerotolerance test performed at the same time as the purity and viability check will help to determine the presence of an aerobic contaminant.

The API 20A (Analytab Products, Inc.) and Minitek (BBL) are microtube biochemical systems that produce results in 24 to 48 hours. The API 20A strip contains 16 carbohydrates and tests for indole, urea, gelatin, esculin, and catalase. The indicator is bromcresol purple, which turns yellow at a pH of 5.2. The Minitek system offers a wide choice of biochemical tests utilizing microtray plates and disks saturated with various substrates. The indicator is phenol red, which turns yellow at pH 6.8. The color reactions in both these systems are not always clearcut; shades of brown (API) and yellow oranges (Minitek) can make interpretation of test results difficult. In this situation neither system should be relied upon for identification. Both systems are not useful for the identification of asaccharolytic organisms; supplemental tests, including GLC, are often necessary for speciation of isolates. Each system has a computerized data base to aid in identification. More trials comparing these microtube systems to the PRAS system are necessary to determine their efficacy.

The Centers for Disease Control (CDC) have developed three quadrant plates (Presumpto plates I, II, and III) that incorporate test substrates into Lombard-Dowell agar medium (36,37). The Anaerobe-tek plate (Flow Laboratories) combines the tests from the three Presumpto plates into a single wheel containing individual agars that test glucose, mannitol, lactose, and trehalose fermentation; esculin, starch, casein and gelatin hydrolysis; and production of hydrogen sulfide, indole, catalase, deoxyribonuclease, lecithinase and lipase; and bile tolerance (98). A computerized data base is available. An unpublished study in our laboratory has shown that the basal medium did not support the growth of approximately 50% of the anaerobes tested and that only 40% of evaluable isolates were correctly identified using PRAS biochemicals as the standard.

The RapID ANA panel (Innovative Diagnostics Systems) is a 4 hour aerobically incubated test system based on the degradation of 18 chromogenic substrates by preformed enzymes. The inoculum consists of a suspension of the test organism in 1 ml of diluent. The turbidity of the inoculum must be equal to that of a #3 McFarland standard. After the ten wells have been scored, reagents are added to eight of the ten and these additional eight tests are read and scored. Gradation in color reactions makes interpretation of some tests moderately difficult. A color chart is provided to aid in interpreting reactions read after the developer is added. A computerized data base is available. Preliminary trials suggest that this system, without the use of GLC or supplemental tests, may be an alternative method for the rapid speciation of common clinical isolates (104, 131). Further comparative trials of the RapID ANA and PRAS biochemical methods, using fresh clinical isolates, will determine the accuracy of this system.

Further comment

It is important to note that a number of anaerobes will not demonstrate the reactions of the described species, so only a genus level or descriptive identification can be designated.

PROCESSING STOOL SPECIMENS FOR *C. DIFFICILE: ISOLATION, IDENTIFICATION AND TOXIN TESTING*

Clostridium difficile is the cause of virtually all cases of pseudomembranous colitis and some cases of antibiotic-associated diarrhea. The laboratory diagnosis currently involves both culture and cytotoxin assay techniques, but the latter is much more important. The development of the selective and differential medium — cycloserine cefoxitin fructose agar (CCFA) — has facilitated isolation and presumptive identification of *C. difficile* from stool specimens (54). Alternative methods using broth cultures, modified CCFA media, and other media have been described (28, 127). *C. difficile* produces two major toxins; an enterotoxin (toxin A) and cytotoxin (toxin B). The tissue culture assays currently in use detect cytotoxin. Lyerly *et al.* and Laughon *et al.* have described ELISA procedures for detecting the enterotoxin of *C. difficile* from stool and culture filtrates (91, 101). Counterimmunoelectrophoresis methods have been described for detecting *C. difficile* cytotoxin, but their usefulness is restricted because of lack of specificity (129, 176, 177). Another promising technique that has been described is a latex agglutination procedure to detect enterotoxin (9). Development of this procedure may provide laboratories with a simple method for detecting enterotoxin.

Culture procedures

Specimen evaluation

Stool specimens less than 2 hours old or frozen at -20° C are acceptable for culture. Rectal swabs are unacceptable.

CCFA medium

The medium is prepared as per directions in the Media and Reagents section, and the plates are stored in plastic bags at 2 to 8°C for up to 8 weeks (39). CCFA plates are also available from various sources.

Specimen processing

1. Specimens are thoroughly mixed and a 2 ml aliquot is reserved for toxin testing. If the cytotoxin tissue culture assay is not done within 24 hours, then the aliquot is frozen at -20° C.
2. Quantitative cultures for *C. difficile* are performed in an anaerobic chamber. 1 g or 1 ml of stool is diluted in 9 ml of a suitable diluent (0.05% yeast extract), and vortexed in tubes containing glass beads, until the suspension appears evenly distributed (approximately 60 seconds). Serial 10-fold dilutions are made and 0.1 ml from dilution tubes 10^{-1}, 10^{-3}, and 10^{-5} are plated onto CCFA using the rotator-pipet method (6). After incubation, the number of colonies on plates containing 30 to 300 colonies are counted. The CFU/ml of stool are calculated by multiplying colony counts times all dilution factors (e.g., 30 colonies on a 10^{-3} plate is 3×10^5 CFU/ml).
3. A semiquantitative culture is done by inoculating approximately 0.1 g or 2 to 3 drops (using a pasteur pipet) of stool onto the first quadrant of a CCFA plate and then streaking for isolation. The grading system as described in the text for clinical specimens is applied (1+ to 4+); this roughly correlates with CFU/ml of stool (4+ $\geq 10^5$ CFU/ml).

4. Plates are incubated anaerobically at 37°C for 24 to 48 hours. If the plates are incubated in a Bio-Bag or anaerobic chamber they can be inspected at 24 hours.

Isolation and Identification

1. *C. difficile* forms distinctive colonies on CCFA. The colonies are approximately 4 mm in diameter (if well isolated), yellow, ground-glass in appearance, circular with a slightly filamentous edge, and low umbonate to flat in profile. The initial orange-pink color of the medium is often changed to yellow for 2 to 3 mm around the colony. *C. difficile* produces a "horse-stable" odor that is detectable from the primary culture plate, but is easier to detect from a pure culture plate. The colonies fluoresce chartreuse (yellow-green) on CCFA, although non-specific chartreuse fluorescence by the inoculum and other anaerobes make this characteristic less distinctive for *C. difficile*. Other organisms may grow on the medium, but their colonies are usually smaller and are unlike the morphology of *C. difficile*. A presumptive report is issued at this time, based on colony morphology.

2. *C. difficile*-like colonies are subcultured to a BA or another CCFA plate for purification and a chocolate agar plate to be incubated in 10% CO_2 for the aerotolerance test, then a slide is prepared to determine the Gram reaction and presence of spores. *C. difficile* readily sporulates on BA but rarely on CCFA. Well isolated colonies are also inoculated into thioglycollate broth (BBL-135C) for subsequent end-product analysis.

3. The pure culture plate is examined for colony morphology, fluorescence, and odor. A thioglycolate broth is inoculated, if not already done, incubated for 48 hours, and then processed for GLC according to methods described in Chapter 4.

Final report

1. A culture is reported as positive for *C. difficile* if a gram-positive sporeforming bacillus with typical colony morphology on CCFA, "horse-stable" odor, chartreuse fluorescence and produces isocaproic acid as one of many end-products. The CFU/ml or CFU/gm dry weight of stool or semiquantitation is also reported.

2. A culture is reported as negative for *C. difficile* if the above criteria are not met.

3. Equivocal isolates may be inoculated into PRAS media for definitive identification.

Toxin testing

Specimen evaluation

1. Stool specimens less than 24 hours old held at room temperature, refrigerated (2 to 8°C), or frozen (-20°C) are acceptable for toxin assay.

2. Stool specimens frozen at -20°C have an unknown but long storage life; Bartlett *et al.* have reported cytotoxin positive stools that had been stored at -40°C for several years (10).

Stool filtrate preparation

1. Liquid specimens or a 1:1 dilution in phosphate buffered saline (PBS pH 7.0) of formed stools are vortexed and then centrifuged at 3,000 g for 20 minutes to produce a clear supernatant. This supernatant is then filtered through a 0.45 μm membrane filter. Known positive and negative stool filtrates are prepared in the same manner and serve as controls.

2. The filtrate is divided into two aliquots.
   a. One aliquot is neutralized with an equal volume of *C. sordellii* or *C. difficile* antitoxin. This control enhances the specificity of the test system.
   b. The second aliquot is untreated or two fold serial dilutions in PBS (pH 7.0) are made if a toxin titer is requested.

Tissue culture preparation (10, 132)

1. HeLa cells (Flow Laboratories) are purchased as monolayers or continuously maintained by splitting the cell line weekly. Other cell lines are also used including primary human amnion, human diploid lung fibroblasts (WI-38), HeP-2, and Chinese hamster ovary cells.

2. The cells are detached from the flask by trypsinization and are suspended in IX Minimum Essential Medium with Earle's salts and glutamine (MEM) (Flow Laboratories) containing 10% fetal calf serum, 20 U of penicillin per ml, and 20 μg of streptomycin per ml. The cell suspension is counted in a hemocytometer and diluted to a final concentration of 50,000 cells per ml. 180 μl is dispensed into each well of a 96 well tissue culture plate. The plate is incubated at 37°C in a 5% CO_2 atmosphere until a confluent or $\geq$70% monolayer of cells is formed (24 hours).

3. The medium is replaced with 180 μl MEM containing 2% fetal calf serum, penicillin (20 U/ml), and streptomycin (20 μg/ml).

4. 20 μl of each stool and control filtrate is transferred to a well, and the panel is incubated at 37°C in a 5% CO_2 atmosphere for 18 to 24 hours.

Interpretation

C. difficile cytotoxin causes detachment of, and actinomorphic changes in, the HeLa cells; that is, the cells round up or string out.

1. A test is considered cytotoxin positive when
   a. a 90% change occurs in the test well as compared to the negative control, *AND*
   b. the neutralized filtrate well appears the same as the negative control. The endpoint of the titration is interpreted as the last well showing a 90% change compared to the negative control.

2. A test is considered cytotoxin negative when:
   a. a <90% change occurs in the test wells as compared to the negative control, *OR*
   b. the neutralized filtrate-containing well shows any change as compared to the negative control.

3. The positive control must also show a 90% change compared to the negative control.

CHAPTER 4

GAS-LIQUID CHROMATOGRAPHY (GLC)

APPLICATIONS AND LIMITATIONS OF GLC IN ANAEROBIC BACTERIOLOGY

Because anaerobic metabolism is not as efficient as that of facultative organisms, intermediate products are left that can serve as markers of an organism's identity. Until end-product analysis became a standard for grouping anaerobes, identification was frequently based on biochemical reactions and morphology, which can vary considerably, depending on the age of the culture and the nutritional composition of the growth medium. Since the enzymes involved are genetically stable, the end-products of an organism's metabolism produce a fingerprint that is typical and useful for identification.

Table 4-1 lists end-products produced by the genera of anaerobes that are commonly isolated from clinical specimens. For discussion of other anaerobes, refer to Chapter 3.

The gram-positive bacilli are readily distinguished, based on their end products. *Propionibacterium* sp. typically produce large amounts of propionic acid. *Actinomyces* sp. produce succinic acid, although the quantity may vary, depending on available carbonate. Acetic acid is also produced; lactic acid is present in some species and absent in others. Members of the genus *Lactobacillus* produce lactic acid as the sole end product. *Bifidobacterium* sp. produce acetic and lactic acids; acetic acid is present in larger quantities than lactic acid. The genus *Eubacterium* is a "catch-all" genus for non-spore-forming gram-positive rods that do not fit the above criteria. Different species within this genus produce a variety of end-products that can be helpful in identifying a specific species, but the genus itself is not strictly defined. The genus *Clostridium* is similar to the genus *Eubacterium* in that any number of end-products may be produced by the different species. Since there are many species of *Clostridium* with similar biochemical reactions, end-product analysis can be very helpful for species level identification.

The genus *Fusobacterium* is defined by the presence of butyric acid and the absence of iso-acids. Lactic acid production varies within the genus. Various species in this genus can also convert threonine or lactate to propionate which is a characteristic helpful for identification. The other commonly encountered

Table 4-1 Metabolic end products of glucose and amino acids in anaerobes commonly encountered clinically

---

Gram positive bacilli

Propionibacterium, Arachnia	A P (L)
Actinomyces	A(S)(L)
Lactobacillus	L
Bifidobacterium	AL
Eubacterium	(A)(IB)(B)(IV)(V)(C)
Clostridium	(A)(P)(IB)(B)(IV)(V)(IC)(C)(L)

Gram negative bacilli

Fusobacterium	A B (L)
Bacteroides	(A)(P)(IB)(B)(IV)(L)(S)
Leptotrichia *	L

Gram positive cocci

Peptostreptococcus asaccharolyticus	A B (L)
P. anaerobius	A (IB)(IV) IC
P. magnus	A
P. micros	A
P. prevotii	A B (L)
P. tetradius	A B L
Streptococcus	L

Gram negative cocci

Veillonella	A P
Acidaminococcus	A B
Megasphaera	A IB B IV V C

Key			
A =	acetic acid	IV =	isovaleric acid
P =	propionic acid	V =	valeric acid
IB =	isobutyric acid	IC =	isocaproic acid
B =	butyric acid	C =	caproic acid
		( ) =	may be present

---

* *Leptotrichia* is infrequently isolated from clinical specimens; its morphology may resemble that of *Fusobacterium nucleatum*

genus of gram-negative rods is *Bacteroides*. Although the different species are capable of producing a variety of end-products, the majority of clinical strains produce acetic and succinic acids. A few species produce butyric acid, but always with isobutyric and isovaleric acids which distinguishes them from *Fusobacterium*. Succinic acid may be absent in some of these species. Production of phenylacetic acid distinguishes *B. gingivalis* from *B. asaccharolyticus*.

The genus *Peptostreptococcus* (including the former genus *Peptococcus* except for *P. niger*) is not defined by specific end-products; however, the species within the genus do have characteristic patterns. Thus, the morphologically and biochemically similar *P. magnus* and *P. prevotii* may be differentiated in that *P. prevotii* produces acetic and butyric acids while *P. magnus* produces only acetic acid. *P. anaerobius* is easily identified by the presence of isocaproic acid.

The three genera of gram-negative cocci have unique end-products. *Veillonella* produces acetic and propionic acids. *Acidaminococcus* has acetic and butyric acids and *Megasphaera* produces iso-acids along with butyric, valeric, and caproic acids.

Thus, one can see that end-product analysis is useful in determining the genus of an organism, as in the case of gram-positive rods, *Fusobacterium*, and gram-negative cocci or the species of an organism, as with gram-positive cocci, some *Clostridium* sp. and some *Bacteroides*. It is not essential for the identification of all anaerobes.

Although an organism's metabolic pathway is a stable characteristic, various factors may affect the actual pattern one measures. A profound variable is the nutritional composition of the medium in which the organism is grown, specifically the carbohydrate/peptone ratio. Glucose is metabolized preferentially by organisms capable of fermenting. Thus, in a peptone-glucose broth, end-products of glucose metabolism such as acetate and butyrate, will be formed first. Iso-acids, formed from metabolism of peptones, will appear more slowly. If an organism is a non-fermenter, the iso-acids will be present in young cultures. Media rich in peptones, such as chopped meat broth, will yield larger amounts of iso-acids than media poorer in peptone, such as thioglycolate broth. Quantities of end-products increase with the age of the culture until nutrients are depleted and growth ceases, so quantities of any product within the same species can vary accordingly. Chopped meat broth contains lactate; thus, any organism capable of converting lactate to propionate (such as *F. necrophorum*) will show a large propionic acid peak from chopped meat broth that is absent in peptone yeast glucose or thioglycolate broths.

Formic acid is produced by many organisms, but we have not found its presence or absence to be of any help in identification. Since it is not necessarily measured by all routine methods, we disregard it.

Culture media may contain trace amounts of some of these acids. Therefore, one should assay an uninoculated incubated broth and subtract any end-products detected from those found in the sample.

CHROMATOGRAPHS, COLUMNS, AND OPERATING CONDITIONS

The most basic and least expensive type of gas chromatograph is one with a thermal conductivity detector (TCD). It requires only helium as a carrier gas and can be used to measure both volatile and non-volatile endproducts. Care must be exercised to keep water out of the sample because it increases the size of the injection peak and may hide an early peak. Flame ionization detector (FID) chromatographs have an advantage in that one can use aqueous samples. However, they require three separate gas tanks: nitrogen as the carrier gas, and air and hydrogen for the flame. There may be restrictions in some institutions on storage of pure hydrogen in the laboratory.

Gas chromatographs suitable for these analyses are available in a wide range of sophistication and price. They may include an automatic injector or a computer which converts peak area to milliequivalent (mEq) quantities. The price will vary accordingly. Highly sophisticated equipment is not required for endproduct analysis where only a semi-quantitative result is needed.

Table 4-2 summarizes columns with which we have had experience. If injecting aqueous samples onto the SP 1220 column, note that ghost peaks may appear from previous samples, especially as the column gets older. Also, some organisms produce alcohols that may elute near fatty acid peaks. We have not found this to be a problem.

Prepacked columns are reasonably priced and are available from a variety of sources. We use the Supelco SP-1000 and SP-1220. Details of these two packings can be found in Bulletin No. 748 from Supelco. Cleaning and repacking a column can be a time-consuming, painful, and frustrating experience for a novice, and we no longer do this in our laboratory.

The separation of fatty acids is achieved by injecting the prepared samples through a septum into the end of a column contained in a heated oven. The high temperature in the injector port volatilizes the sample and the flow of the carrier gas moves the sample down the length of the column, separating the fatty acids according to molecular weight and polarity. When a fatty acid reaches the detec-

Table 4-2 Suggested columns

Column	Detector	Volatile fatty acids detected	Non-volatile fatty acids detected	Other
SP-1000[1]	TCD	Yes	Yes	Formic
SP-1220[2]	FID	Yes	Yes	

[1] 10% SP-1000/1% H_3PO_4 on chrom W A W, 100-120 mesh, Supelco
[2] 15% SP-1220/1% H_3PO_4 on chrom W A W, 100-120 mesh, Supelco

tor it causes an electrical response which is converted by the recorder to a peak on the chart. The more fatty acid present, the larger the peak, both in height and width. The retention time (the length of time from injection of the sample to detection of the peak) determines the identity of the peak as compared to a standard of known fatty acid composition. Increasing carrier gas flow rate decreases retention time for all peaks as they simply get pushed out more rapidly; however, peak separation (resolution) decreases. Increasing the oven temperature has the same effect.

Figure 4-1 shows the patterns of the volatile and non-volatile fatty acid standards (available from Supelco).

The operating parameters listed in Table 4-3 serve as a guide. We have found that with a new column, carrier gas flow rate is on the low side, as is oven temperature. As a column gets older and residues clog the entry, efficiency is often improved by increasing the carrier gas flow rate by a few ml/minute or increasing the temperatures of the injector, oven and detector by 5 to 10°C, always being careful not to exceed the maximum tolerated temperature of the column, as specified by the manufacturer. When changes of this sort are made, it is essential to run the standard to determine that all peaks are present and well separated.

PREPARATION OF SAMPLES FOR ANALYSIS

Broth cultures are acidified to pH 2 with 2 drops of 50% H_2SO_4 added to 5 ml of broth. The tubes are centrifuged and the clear supernatant is removed. Once the sample is acidified, the end-products remain stable for several months in the refrigerator.

For determination of volatile fatty acids, 1 μl of the supernatant may be injected as is, if an FID with an SP-1220 or SP-1000 column is being used. If a TCD is used, the sample must be extracted as follows:

1. Pipet 1 ml of supernatant into a glass tube.
2. Add 0.2 ml 50% H_2SO_4, 0.4 gm NaCl, and 1 ml methyl-t-butyl ether. (Methyl-t-butyl ether is preferable to ethyl ether because it has a higher boiling point. It is manufactured by Burdick and Jackson.)
3. Stopper tube and mix well by inverting approximately 20 times.
4. Centrifuge briefly or allow to stand for approximately 1/2 hour to separate the water/ether layers.
5. Remove the ether layer to another tube and add a pinch of 4-20 mesh anhydrous $CaCl_2$ to remove traces of water. Shake gently and allow to stand for a few minutes. The sample is now ready for injection.
6. The amount of sample to be injected varies with the column and operating conditions. One should experiment with the standard and determine the optimum amount. It may vary from 5 to 15 μl. The injection peak should not obscure peaks of interest.

For determination of non-volatile acids, methyl derivatives must be prepared as follows:

1. Pipet 1 ml of supernatant into a glass tube.

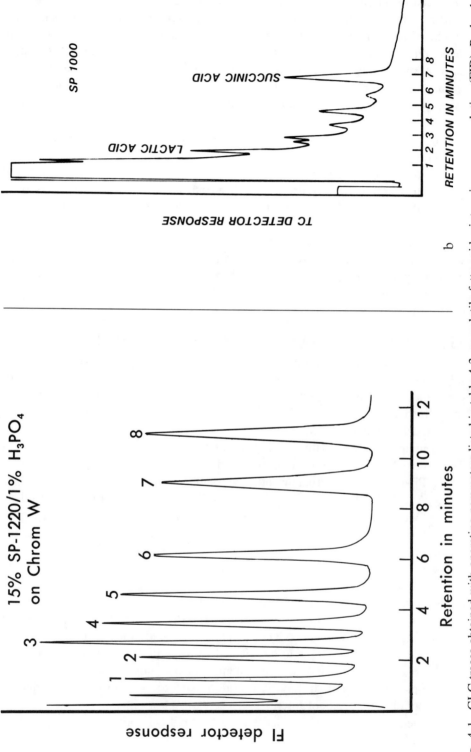

Fig. 4-1. GLC traces obtained with operating parameters listed in table 4-3. a. volatile fatty acid mixture in aqueous solution (FID). Peaks: 1, acetic acid; 2, propionic acid; 3, isobutyric acid; 4, n-butyric acid; 5, isovaleric acid; 6, n-valeric acid; 7, isocaproic acid; 8, n-caproic acid. b. methyl esters of non-volatile acids in chloroform (TCD).

Table 4-3 Operating parameters

	FID	TCD
Column packing	SP 1220	SP 1000
Gases	N$_2$ 30 ml/min H$_2$ 25 ml/min Air 300 ml/min	He 100 ml/min
Injection temp. (°C)	150 - 180	150 - 180
Detector temp. (°C)	150 - 180	150 - 180
Oven temp. (°C)	140 - 170	140 - 170
TCD filament	—	200 m amp.
attenuation	—	1:2 - 1:4
FID range	10	—
attenuation	x 128 - 8	—
Recorder range	1 mv full scale	1 mv full scale
Chart speed	1/2″/min or 1 cm/min	1/2″/min or 1 cm/min

2. Add 2 ml methanol and 0.4 ml 50% H$_2$SO$_4$.
3. Stopper tubes, shake vigorously and heat at 60°C for 30 minutes or allow to stand at room temperature overnight.
4. Add 1 ml water and 0.5 ml chloroform, replace stopper, and mix well. If the sample is heated, cool it to room temperature before adding chloroform.
5. Allow to stand for a few minutes or centrifuge briefly to separate the chloroform/water layers.
6. Draw the bottom chloroform layer into the syringe, wipe the outside of the needle, and inject into the column. The amount of sample to be injected will vary with the column and operating conditions. Too large a sample may obscure significant peaks. One should use a standard, extracted in the same manner, to determine the optimum amount. The range is usually 3 to 14 μl.

OTHER APPLICATIONS OF GLC

End-product analysis may also be performed directly on pus or infected body fluids (59, 60, 109, 128, 148). These specimens are preferably extracted into ether as it is often difficult to prepare a sufficiently clean supernatant for direct injection into an FID chromatograph. This procedure can sometimes provide rapid presumptive identification of anaerobes present, or can serve to distinguish an anaerobic from an aerobic infection. If many types of organisms are present, it may be difficult to determine which organism is producing which end-product. For example, if gram-positive cocci and gram-negative bacilli are present on the Gram stain, and butyric acid is found, one can infer that *P. prevotii*, *P. asaccharolyticus*, *P. tetradius*, and/or *Fusobacterium* sp are present. If butyric acid is not found, one could infer that other *Peptostreptococcus* sp or facultative gram positive cocci are present, and that the gram negative bacillus is not a *Fusobacterium*. If gram negative bacilli and gram positive bacilli are noted on gram stain, and iso-acids are found, they may be from a *Bacteroides* sp or a *Clostridium* or *Eubacterium* sp. It has been our experience that a careful reading of a gram stain usually yields just as much information as end-product analysis when several types of organisms are present. If only one organism is present, such as in blood culture bottles, end-product analysis is often very helpful.

End-product analysis can also be a useful aid in determining the presence of ''non-specific vaginitis'' which is associated with the presence of succinate-producing *Bacteroides* sp and butyrate-producing gram positive cocci, and the absence of lactate-producing *Lactobacillus* sp (126,150). A vaginal wash sample is prepared, using 4 ml of sterile saline. The sample is then acidified and a 1 ml aliquot is extracted into ether for measurement of the volatile acids, and another aliquot is methylated to detect the non-volatile lactic and succinic acids.

Hydrogen Gas

Although the presence or absence of hydrogen gas is not routinely used in the identification of clinical isolates of anaerobes, it may be helpful in some instances. It requires a different column from those used to identify fatty acids. The column is silica gel D-08, 80-100 mesh (Applied Sciences) and the detector is a TCD. The organism is grown in PY fructose in a tube that permits insertion of a 1-1/2" $\times$ 22 gauge needle to remove the head space gas. The syringe must be airtight and purged with nitrogen. The carrier gas is nitrogen at 45 ml/min. The injector and oven temperature is 45°C. The filament is set at 100 ma, attenuation at $\times$ 1. Under these conditions, hydrogen elutes at about 2 minutes, just ahead of oxygen.

CHAPTER 5

SUSCEPTIBILITY TESTING OF ANAEROBES

Antimicrobial therapy of anaerobic infections is usually determined empirically because cultivation and isolation of clinically important anaerobic bacteria are relatively slow, and results of susceptibility tests are usually not available for 2 to 4 days. For the most part, this is a satisfactory approach, because with many anaerobes there is a reasonable level of predictability of antimicrobial susceptibility that serves as the basis for selection of appropriate initial therapy. Current patterns of susceptibility of anaerobes to antimicrobial agents are shown in Tables 5-1 to 5-3.

Routine susceptibility testing of all anaerobic isolates is not recommended, but there are a number of circumstances when determination of the susceptibility of individual isolates is of great importance. Susceptibility tests are usually needed for patients with serious infections such as endocarditis or brain abscess or infections requiring prolonged therapy such as osteomyelitis, or in infections that persist or recur despite appropriate empiric antimicrobial therapy. Tests are also needed to monitor the susceptibility of commonly isolated species so that changing patterns of resistance can be detected and the empirical basis of therapy can reflect any changes in antibiogram.

Methods similar to those used for aerobic and facultative bacteria are useful for estimating the susceptibility of anaerobes to various antimicrobial agents. Broth dilution tests, both macro- and micro-, and agar dilution tests are currently being used. Agar diffusion tests are not recommended because of the complexities and variation introduced by the slow and varying growth rates of anaerobic bacteria.

BROTH DILUTION TESTS
Macrodilution test

Conventional broth dilution tests are convenient if small numbers of strains are to be tested or if the bacteria, such as *Clostridium* sp., spread on the surface of agar plates. They are also useful if one wishes to determine bactericidal as well as bacteriostatic activity of a drug. Dilutions of the drug are prepared in a suitable medium. If the medium is not kept under reduced conditions, it should be boiled out or reduced in an anaerobic atmosphere prior to use. An inoculum

Table 5-1 *In vitro* susceptibility of anaerobes to antimicrobial agents

Bacteria	Chloramphenicol	Clindamycin	Erythromycin†	Metronidazole	Cefoxitin	Ureido-and carboxypenicillins[a]	Penicillin G‡	Tetracycline	Vancomycin†
Anaerobic cocci	+++	++ to +++	++ to +++	+++[c]*	+++	+++	+++	+ to ++	+++
B. fragilis group	+++	++ to +++	+ to ++	+++	++ to +++	++ to +++	+	+ to ++	+
Other *Bacteroides* sp.	+++	+++[c]	++ to +++	+++	+++[c]	+++[c]	++ to +++	++	+
F. varium	+++	+ to ++	+	+++	+++[c]	+++[c]	+++[c]	++	+
Other *Fusobacterium* sp.	+++	+++	+	+++	+++[b]	+++[b]	++++	+++	+
C. perfringens	+++	+++[b]	+++	+++	+++	+++	+++	++	+++
Other *Clostridium* sp.	+++	++	++ to +++	+++	+ to ++	+++	+++	++	++ to +++
Nonsporeforming GPR	+++	++ to +++	+++	+ to ++	+++	+++	++++	++ to +++	++ to +++

Key
+ = Poor or inconsistent activity; ++ = moderate activity; +++ = good activity; ++++ = good activity, good pharmacologic characteristics, low toxicity, drug of choice

a Piperacillin, mezlocillin, azlocillin, carbenicillin, ticarcillin
b Rare strains are resistant
c A few strains are resistant
† Not approved by FDA for anaerobic infections
* Microaerophilic streptococci (officially in the genus *Streptococcus*) are often resistant to metronidazole
‡ Other penicillins and cephalosporins are frequently less active. Ampicillin and amoxicillin are roughly comparable to penicillin G in activity. Addition of beta-lactamase inhibitors such as clavulanic acid and sulbactam, remarkably increase the activity against beta-lactamase producers such as the *B. fragilis* group

Table 5-2 Percent of various anaerobes susceptible* to most active presently available antimicrobial agents

Breakpoint (μg/ml)	Antimicrobial agents	Bacteroides fragilis group	Other Bacteroides species	Fusobacterium species	Anaerobic cocci	Clostridium	Actino- myces and Arachnia
16	Metronidazole	100	100	100	98-99	99	25
16	Chloramphenicol	100	100	100	100	100	100
4	Clindamycin	95	97	98	97	90	100
128	Piperacillin-mezlocillin-azlocillin	95	96	99	100	100	100
128	Carbenicillin-ticarcillin	95	96	99	100	100	100
32	Cefoxitin	95	96	99	100	65	100

* At breakpoint

Table 5-3 Susceptibility of *B. fragilis* group to other beta-lactam antimicrobial
agents.

Antimicrobial agent	% Susceptible at Breakpoint
Imipenem, Sch 34343	100
Cefoperazone, moxalactam, apalcillin	~70
Cefotaxime, cefmenoxime, ceftazidime, cefotetan, cefbuperazone	~50
Ceftizoxime, ceftriaxone, cefpiramide	~30
Cefuroxime, cephalothin, cefazolin, cefonicid	5-15

is added so that the final concentration of bacteria is between 10^5 and 10^6
CFU/ml.

The procedure is as follows: serial two-fold dilutions of the antimicrobial
agent are prepared in Brucella broth containing Fildes enrichment (5%) or hemin
(5 μg/ml) and vitamin K_1 (0.1 μg/ml). A limited number of concentrations of
drugs that are clinically relevant may be selected to simplify the procedure. Table
5-4 indicates solvents for stock solutions of antibiotics. With rapidly growing
strains, the inoculum is prepared as follows:

1. Three or four colonies or a 3 mm loopful of the strain to be tested are
   picked from an overnight culture on a blood agar plate and inoculated into
   a tube of 5 to 6 ml supplemented thioglycollate medium without indicator
   (BBL 135 C). This medium is enriched with hemin (5 μg/ml) and vitamin K_1 (0.1 μg/ml) prior to sterilization plus $NaHCO_3$ (1 mg/ml) added
   just prior to use. This medium will henceforth be referred to as THCK.
2. After a 4- to 6-h incubation at 37°C, the culture is diluted in Brucella
   broth (supplemented as above) to the turbidity of the 0.5 McFarland standard (10^8 CFU/ml), and is then further diluted 1:200.

With slower growing strains, colonies are picked from a 2- to 3-day-old
blood agar plate culture, inoculated into THCK, and incubated overnight prior to
dilution (as above) for the test.

A volume of inoculum equal to the amount of broth containing the drug is
added, and tests are incubated at 37°C in GasPak jars for approximately 48
hours. An inoculated broth containing no antimicrobial agent is included as a
growth control for each strain tested and a tube of uninoculated broth is also
included with each day's tests. Tests on control strains of known susceptibility
should also be included. The minimum inhibitory concentration (MIC) is read as
the lowest concentration of drug showing no visible growth.

Bactericidal endpoints are determined by streaking 0.1 ml of material from
each tube to a blood agar plate. Plates are incubated anaerobically for 48 hours

Table 5-4 Solvents for stock solutions of antimicrobial agents

Antimicrobial Agent	Solvent	Antimicrobial Agent	Solvent
Ampicillin	Phosphate buffer 0.1 M, pH 8	Chloramphenicol	Phosphate buffer 0.1 M, pH 6
Carbenicillin (and other similar broad spectrum penicillins)	Water	Clindamycin	Water
		Erythromycin	Ethanol[a]
		Imipenem	Phosphate buffer 0.01 M, pH 7.2
Cefamandole	Water	Metronidazole	Water
Cefoperazone	Water	Moxalactam	Water
Cefotaxime	Water	Penicillin G	Water
Cefoxitin	Water	Tetracycline	Water
Cephalothin	Phosphate buffer, 0.1 M, pH 8	Vancomycin	0.05 N HCl[b]

[a] Erythromycin is dissolved in 1/10 of final volume 95% ethanol, then brought to the proper volume with water.
[b] Stock solution is made with 0.05 N HCl, further dilutions are made in water.

and the minimum bactericidal concentration (MBC) is read as the lowest concentration of drug resulting in fewer than 25 colonies (99.9% killing rate).

Microdilution test

Microdilution tests are miniaturized variations of the broth dilution procedure described previously. A variety of manual, semiautomated, and automated devices are available which allow the preparation of large numbers of two-fold dilution series of antimicrobial agents economically and rapidly.

Plastic trays containing eight or more rows of small, flat-bottomed U- or V-shaped wells are used. Dilutions may be prepared by adding 50 μl of broth to each well with one of several varieties of dispensing pipets or semiautomated dispensers. Special calibrated loops are then used to transfer 50 μl of stock solutions of antimicrobial agents to the first well of each row, then the contents of these wells are mixed by twirling the loops. Next, 50 μl are transferred to the wells in the second row, mixed, transferred to the next row of wells and continued until the dilution series is completed. Alternatively, a multichannel dispenser may be used to dispense 50 or 100 μl of dilutions of antimicrobial agents to the wells of the trays.

After trays are filled, they may be sealed and frozen at -20°C or colder. Self-defrosting freezer units should not be used since the fluctuation of temperature during the defrost cycle contributes to rapid deterioration of the antimicrobial agents. Trays stored at -20°C are stable for up to 4 months; trays stored at -60°C are stable for up to a year. Quality control must be performed periodically to monitor shelf life.

The inoculum is grown in the same manner as for the broth dilution test, adjusted to the turbidity of the 0.5 McFarland standard, and is then further diluted so that the final density of bacteria in each well is approximately 10^5 to 10^6 CFU/ml. The exact dilution used will vary depending upon the volume of broth in the wells and the volume of inoculum delivered. Alternatively, a suspension may be prepared from growth on a plate not more than 72 hours old, adjusting the density as previously noted (115, 116). The authors of the references cited feel that better results are obtained in this way. Preliminary work in our laboratory confirms these observations.

Trays are removed from the freezer, allowed to thaw, and then inoculated (any unused trays should be discarded, never refrozen). Thawing and preconditioning the plates in an anaerobic atmosphere for 4 hours or more will enhance the growth of some of the more fastidious anaerobes but is usually not necessary for strains of the *B. fragilis* group. When metronidazole is part of the test system, trays must be preconditioned to ensure optimum activity of metronidazole.

Tests are incubated in an anaerobic jar for 48 hours. The MIC is read as the lowest concentration of drug showing no visible growth. Interpretation of the endpoint with some of the cephalosporins against some strains of the *B. fragilis* group can be difficult since there sometimes is a small button of growth in several wells beyond the larger button exhibited in the growth control well. Our practice has been to read the endpoint as the concentration in the well where a drastic change in the size of the button occurs. With metronidazole a tiny button of precipitate occurs in all wells. Again, the endpoint is read as the concentration in the well where a drastic change in the size of the button occurs.

Commercially prepared frozen trays are available from Micro-Media Systems. These have been shown to be satisfactory and are convenient for the laboratory which does small numbers of tests (83). Other systems, utilizing lyophilized antimicrobial agents, are being developed, but are not yet approved for use with anaerobes. When commercially available test trays are used the manufacturer's directions for test performance and quality control should be followed for reliable, reproducible results.

BROTH-DISK TESTS

Modifications of broth tests that simplify procedures for microbiologists in clinical laboratories have been gaining widespread acceptance. Selected concentrations of antimicrobial agents relevant to the clinical situation are incorporated into liquid media by means of elution from paper disks.

A practical procedure described by Kurzynski and co-workers places antimicrobial agent disks into thioglycollate medium (BBL 135C) prepared in screw-capped tubes and incubates the tests under aerobic conditions (68a,90). For strains of pigmented *Bacteroides,* a 0.5 ml supplement of nine parts of rabbit serum and one part of hemin-menadione stock solution (500 μg of hemin, 50 μg of menadione) is added.

Disks are added to the thioglycolate medium as indicated in Table 5-5. Tubes are inoculated with 0.1 ml of an actively growing culture of the organism (24 to 48 hours) to be tested. Alternatively, several colonies picked from a plate not more than 72 hours old may be suspended in a broth medium to achieve a 0.5 McFarland standard or greater. One tube of medium without antibiotic should be inoculated with each organism tested to serve as a growth control. After inoculation, tubes are gently inverted 2 or 3 times to ensure adequate mixing of antibiotic and inoculum. Tubes are incubated for 18 to 24 hours (occasionally 48 hours may be required). Susceptibility to the drugs is indicated by the absence of growth or less than 50% of the growth as compared to the control tube.

AGAR DILUTION TESTS
Wadsworth Method

Agar dilution tests are convenient when large numbers of strains are to be tested. Test results are often easier to read, and there is the advantage of visual detection of contaminants. Dilutions of drugs are prepared and incorporated into Brucella agar supplemented with vitamin K_1 and either 5% defibrinated sheep blood or 5% defibrinated sheep blood that has been laked (lysed) by freezing and thawing. The concentrations of antimicrobial agents may be made in a series of two-fold dilutions (Table 5-6) or may be a set of concentrations relevant to the clinical situation (67).

Table 5-5 Preparation of broth-disk tubes

Drugs	Disk Content[b]	No. of disks 5 ml medium	Test concentration/ml[a,b]
Ampicillin	10	2	4
Carbenicillin	100	3	60
Cefoperazone	75	2	30
Other cephalosporins[c]	30	3	18
Chloramphenicol	30	3	18
	30	2	12
Clindamycin[d]	2	8	3.2
	2	4	1.6
Metronidazole	80	1	16
Mezlocillin	75	4	60
Penicillin G	10	1	2
Piperacillin	100	3	60
Tetracycline	5	3	3
Ticarcillin	75	4	60

[a] Concentrations listed are not always the same as those recommended by Kurzynski and co-workers (68a, 90). Other concentrations can be obtained by altering the number of disks or the volume of medium. If more than 4 disks are used, they should be reduced prior to addition to the medium.

[b] Content or concentration in μg/ml except for penicillin G which is in u/ml.

[c] Includes cefamandole, cefotaxime, cefoxitin, moxalactam.

[d] A 10 μg disk may become available and would be preferable. Two 10 μg disks added to 5 ml of medium will give a concentration of 4 μg/ml. One 10 μg disk added to 5 ml of medium will give a concentration of 2 μg/ml. If oral therapy is to be used, the lower concentration should be tested.

The inoculum is grown in the same manner as for the broth dilution test, adjusted to the turbidity of the 0.5 McFarland standard and applied to the plates without further dilution. The inoculum is applied by means of a Steers' replicator (Craft Machine, Inc.). Two plates of the medium being used in the tests should be inoculated prior to and after stamping each series of antimicrobial agent-containing medium as controls. One of these is incubated along with the tests to serve as a growth control; the other is incubated aerobically to detect aerobic contamination. Strains of known susceptibility should be included as controls. Table 5-7 indicates mode MICs and ranges obtained with ATCC 29327 and ATCC 29328 for several antimicrobial agents when tested by this method. The test and growth control plates are incubated anaerobically at 37°C in Gas-Pak jars for approximately 48 hours. The MIC is read as the lowest concentration of drug yielding no growth, a barely visible haze, or one discrete colony.

The definition of endpoints with some antimicrobial agents (particularly beta-lactams) and some bacteria (some members of the *B. fragilis* group and some *Fusobacterium* species) is very difficult. There is often a trailing effect which may continue to the end of the dilution series as in the microdilution method. Again, our practice has been to read the inhibitory concentration as that concentration where a drastic change occurs in the appearance of growth as compared to that on the control plate.

Approved Reference Method

An agar dilution procedure has been accepted by the National Committee for Clinical Laboratory Standards (119). The procedure is intended as a reference method to which other methods may be compared and standardized. It cannot be recommended for general routine use. The medium used does not support the growth of all clinically important anaerobes. Even with the addition of blood, some strains of *Bacteroides* sp. and *Fusobacterium* sp. do not grow or grow so poorly that results cannot be considered reliable.

Table 5-6 Preparation of dilutions (agar dilution tests)

	Concentration (μg or U)	Final Concentration (μg or U/ml when 2 ml added to 18 ml agar)
Stock*	2,560	256
4 ml 2560 + 4	1,280	128
2 ml 2560 + 6	640	64
2 ml 2560 + 14	320	32
4 ml 320 + 4	160	16
2 ml 320 + 6	80	8
2 ml 320 + 14	40	4
4 ml 40 + 4	20	2
2 ml 40 + 6	10	1
2 ml 40 + 14	5	0.5
4 ml 5 + 4	2.5	0.25
2 ml 5 + 6	1.25	0.125
2 ml 5 + 14	0.62	0.062
4 ml 0.62 + 4	0.31	0.031
2 ml 0.62 + 6	0.15	0.015

* In μg/ml or U/ml + ml H_2O

Table 5-7 Modes and ranges of MICs with Wadsworth control strains using Wadsworth method

Antimicrobial Agent	*Bacteroides vulgatus* ATCC #29327		*Peptostreptococcus magnus* ATCC #29328	
	Mode MIC	Range	Mode MIC	Range
Ampicillin	1	1-2	0.125	0.125-0.25
Carbenicillin	0.5	0.125-1	0.5	0.25-1
Cefoxitin	1	0.5-1	0.25	0.125-0.5
Cephalothin	8	2-8	0.25	0.125-0.5
Chloramphenicol	2	2-4	2	2-4
Clindamycin	≤ 0.063	≤ 0.063-0.125	0.5	0.5-1
Doxycycline	2	2-4	0.25	≤ 0.063-2
Erythromycin	0.5	0.25-2	2	0.5-4
Metronidazole	1	0.125-2	0.5	0.25-2
Penicillin G	1	0.5-2	≤ 0.063	≤ 0.063-0.125
Tetracycline	8	4-16	0.5	0.25-1
Vancomycin	8	4-8	0.125	0.125-0.25

Antimicrobial agents are prepared and incorporated into Wilkins-Chalgren agar as suggested by Ericsson and Sherris (42). Stock solutions containing 2,560 μg/ml are prepared in water or other diluent, diluted, and then incorporated into agar (Table 5-6).

The inoculum is prepared by growing each test strain on Brucella blood agar for 48 to 72 hours. If the test strain is reconstituted from lyophilized or frozen stock, it should be transferred to fresh blood agar plates at least twice before the test is performed. Portions of five colonies or more to provide a 3 mm loopful of growth are inoculated into 5 to 6 ml of THCK and incubated 18 to 20 hours. Just prior to the test, the turbidity is adjusted to that of the 0.5 McFarland standard with clear Brucella broth (boiled and cooled prior to use). Alternatively, several colonies may be suspended in broth to achieve the turbidity of the 0.5 McFarland standard. The source plate used for this method must not be older than 72 hours and must not remain at ambient atmosphere for more than 30 minutes (115, 116). The inoculum is applied by means of a Steers' replicator and the inoculated plates incubated in GasPak jars for 48 hours. At the beginning and end of each series of antibiotic dilutions, two plates of Wilkins-Chalgren agar are inoculated. One set of plates is incubated along with the tests as growth controls, and the other set is incubated aerobically to detect possible aerobic contamination during the course of the procedure. Control strains of known susceptibility should be included in the test. Three strains have been recommended: *C. perfringens,* ATCC #13124; *B. fragilis*, ATCC #25285; and *B. thetaiotaomicron*, ATCC #29741. Mode MICs and ranges obtained with these strains and nine antibiotics are shown in Table 5-8.

The MIC of each strain is the lowest concentration of drug yielding no growth, one discrete colony or a barely visible haze as determined by the unaided eye. The barely visible haze is sometimes described as 80% inhibition. This is usually observed as a distinct inhibition of growth as compared with the growth control.

BETA-LACTAMASE TEST

In many instances the production of beta-lactamase enzymes is predictive of resistance to beta-lactam antibiotics. A beta-lactamase test can be used as a rapid supplement to conventional susceptibility tests. Because resistance to beta-lactam antibiotics has been reported in some organisms that do not produce beta-lactamase, this test should be used as an adjunct and not a replacement for conventional susceptibility tests. Table 5-9 lists anaerobes that have been found to produce beta-lactamase.

The most reliable method for detecting beta-lactamases in anaerobic bacteria utilizes the chromogenic cephalosporin, nitrocefin. Disks impregnated with nitrocefin are available as Cefinase™ from BBL.

The test is performed by moistening a disk with sterile water, and then smearing several well isolated colonies onto the disk with a sterile loop or applicator stick. A positive reaction is indicated by a color change from yellow to red within 5 to 10 minutes.

Table 5-8 Acceptable ranges of MICs for NCCLS control strains using reference method[a]

Antimibrobial Agent	*Bacteroides fragilis* ATCC #25285	*Bacteroides thetaiotaomicron* ATCC #29741	*Clostridium perfringens* ATCC #13124
Carbenicillin	16-64[b]	16-64	0.25-1
Cefamandole	32-128	32-128	0.063-0.25
Cefoperazone	32-64	32-128	NR[c]
Cefotaxime	8-32	16-64	0.063-0.25
Cefoxitin	4-16	8-32	0.25-1
Chloramphenicol	2-8	4-16	2-8
Clindamycin	0.5-2	2-8	0.031-0.125
Imipenem	0.031-0.125	0.063-0.25	0.031-0.063
Metronidazole	0.25-1	0.5-2	0.125-0.5
Mezlocillin	16-64	8-32	0.063-0.25
Moxalactam	0.25-1	4-16	0.031-0.125
Penicillin G	16-64	16-64	0.063-0.25
Tetracycline	0.125-0.5	8-32	0.031-0.125
Ticarcillin	16-64	16-64	0.25-1

[a] Data from Sutter *et al.* (157), Zabransky *et al.* (184), and Zabransky *et al.* (185)
[b] MIC in μg/ml except for penicillin G which is U/ml
[c] NR — No range has been recommended with this organism/antimicrobial agent combination.

Table 5-9 Beta-lactamase producing anaerobes*

Bacteroides fragilis group	*B. splanchnicus*
Pigmented *Bacteroides*	*Fusobacterium nucleatum*
B. oralis group	*Megamonas hypermegas*
B. coagulans	*Mitsuokella multiacidus*
B. bivius	*Clostridium ramosum*
B. disiens	*C. clostridiiforme*
B. "ruminicola" group	*C. butyricum*
(*B. oris*, *B. buccae*)	

* Some, but not all strains of these species produce beta-lactamase.

APPENDIX

PITFALLS IN ANAEROBIC BACTERIOLOGY

The following are common errors made in obtaining and processing clinical specimens.

1. Gram stain not prepared directly from clinical specimen. The Gram stain alerts one to the possible presence of organisms requiring special media or conditions of incubation. It also helps one to realize that the techniques are defective if the organisms seen on the smear fail to grow out.
2. Failure to bypass normal flora in collecting specimen.
3. Failure to set up anaerobic cultures promptly from clinical specimens — or to keep these under anaerobic conditions pending culture.
4. Use of fluid thioglycolate or other liquid medium as the only system for growing anaerobes. A number of anaerobes will not grow in thioglycolate medium, even when it is enriched, and solid media are required to separate the various organisms present in mixed culture. Errors are made at times even when anaerobes have grown in fluid thioglycolate medium. Some workers do not check this medium if growth appears on aerobic plates, assuming that the same organism is growing in both. A Gram stain of the broth often alerts one to the additional presence of anaerobes. Rapidly growing aerobes will overgrow the anaerobes making recovery difficult. This procedure delays culture results when anaerobes are present.
5. Use of inadequate commercial media. Failure to use fresh media.
6. Failure to use supplements in media. Vitamin K_1 is required by some strains of *B. melaninogenicus* and may stimulate *B. fragilis*.
7. Failure to use selective media. Some anaerobes may be overgrown by facultative anaerobes and overlooked if selective media are not used.
8. Failure to use a good anaerobic jar.
9. Failure to check jars carefully for leaks after they are set up. Plastic lids are prone to cracking.
10. Catalysts not in good working order when using hydrogen in jars.
11. Using toxic gas in displacement procedure.
12. Failure to include CO_2 in jars. Carbon dioxide is essential for some anaerobes.
13. Failure to hold cultures for extended periods. Occasionally, fastidious organisms present in small numbers may require 5 to 7 days to grow on a plate.
14. Failure to minimize air exposure during processing.
15. Failure to use redox indicator or known fastidious anaerobe in jar.
16. Inaccurate identification and speciation.
17. Use of disk susceptibility technique without standard (or use of Kirby-Bauer aerobic standards).
18. Failure to determine whether organism is a true anaerobe.

Some of the more commonly encountered errors in identification are discussed in the next few paragraphs.

A frequent error is inadequate aerotolerance testing of an organism. Many of the more fastidious unusual aerobic gram-negative bacilli grow slowly, requiring 48 hours to appear on a plate. Thus the following misidentifications have been made:

1. *Actinobacillus actinomycetemcomitans* as *Bacteroides* sp.
2. *Haemophilus aphrophilus* as *B. ureolyticus*
3. *Eikenella corrodens* as *B. ureolyticus*
4. *Capnocytophaga* sp. as *F. nucleatum*
5. *Mycoplasma hominis* as *B. pneumosintes*

Another error is use of a non-viable organism to inoculate biochemicals and then reading the results as valid negatives. A variety of *Bacteroides* sp. have been misidentified as *B. pneumosintes* despite large cell size; *B. pneumosintes* is very tiny.

Misinterpretation of a Gram reaction may also result in error. An organism was submitted to our laboratory as " *Streptococcus intermedius*"; on testing it was found to be *B. bivius*. Volatile fatty acids, measured by gas chromatography, showed some acetic acid. However, methylation for non-volatiles had not been performed; thus the presence of succinate and absence of lactate were missed. The carbohydrate fermentation pattern of *S. intermedius* is not unlike that of *B. bivius*, especially if only a few carbohydrates are tested, and on Gram stain, both organisms are coccobacillary. *B. bivius* is not listed on all charts commonly used for identifying organisms and therefore could be overlooked easily.

Another example of this is the misidentification of gram-negative staining *Clostridium* sp., especially *C. clostridiiforme*, as *Bacteroides*. These *Clostridium* sp. grow well in 20% bile. Use of the antibiotic disks for presumptive identification would indicate a gram-positive organism. The *Clostridium* sp. are vancomycin susceptible and usually kanamycin susceptible and resistant to colistin. *B. fragilis* is resistant to all three antibiotics. Gas chromatography would also provide differentiation.

Several *Bacteroides* sp., especially *B. bivius*, *B. disiens*, and members of the *B. oralis* group, appear quite similar to *B. fragilis* biochemically. Growth in 20% bile is a key reaction for separating these organisms. Failure to inoculate bile has resulted in misidentification of *B. bivius* and members of the *B. oralis* group as *B. fragilis* and *B. oris* or *B. buccae* as *B. vulgatus*.

Failure to obtain pure cultures (and this is difficult at times with anaerobes) also may cause erroneous identification.

SPECIAL QUANTITATIVE FLORA STUDIES
Intestinal flora

Collection and transport

1. Fecal specimens. The specimen should be passed naturally and the entire specimen collected into a plastic container. A small amount of blood on

the outside of the specimen (from rectal bleeding) is allowable. If large amounts are present, the specimen cannot be considered for normal flora studies. Specimens contaminated with urine or menstrual flow are to be rejected.

The specimen container should immediately be placed into an anaerobic chamber or an anaerobic jar with top loosened if the specimen is to be transported. Total flora specimens should not be frozen as freezing kills many vegetative cells. Specimens should be maintained at room temperature no longer than 5 hours if they cannot be processed immediately.

2. Other specimens of intestinal contents. Specimens from the small bowel or other areas of the bowel are usually collected by syringe through a tube passed into the area to be sampled. The tube should be passed through the nose rather than the mouth. The specimen should be placed into a gassed-out tube or anaerobic transport tube.

Processing of specimens

The directions that follow are used for fecal specimens. These may be modified as necessary for other specimens of intestinal contents.

1. The specimen, container, and transporter are weighed, and the weight of the empty transporter and container subtracted from the total weight. The transporter (with specimen inside) is then placed into the anaerobic chamber.
2. After the specimen is in the chamber, it is homogenized as follows:
   a) A Waring stainless steel container with screw cover (Eberbach #8520) is used for specimens 60 g or over. The Eberbach glass container (#8470) is used for stools between 30 and 60 g, and the semimicro jar (Eberbach #8580) is used for solid specimens under 30 g and for liquid specimens under 40 g.

   Non-liquid specimens are blended six times for 30 seconds each time. Intermittent blending is necessary so that a sterile glass rod can be introduced into the blender between each blending operation to scrape the material from the sides of the container and to place it at the bottom of the vessel. This procedure is not necessary with liquid specimens; a continuous 3 minute blending is sufficient with these specimens.

   b) Alternatively, the specimen may be placed into a special plastic bag and blended in the Stomacher (Dynatech Laboratories, Inc.). This method reduces the potential aerosols created by a Waring blender and makes disposal of the unused specimen easier.
3. An aliquot of approximately 1 g of the homogenized specimen is removed from the chamber and placed on a planchet for weighing and drying. Drying is carried out in a vacuum drying oven (15 inch Hg vaccum) with calcium chloride over 48 hours. The specimen is weighed again following drying. The wet/dry weight ratio is determined so that counts obtained may be corrected and expressed as number of organisms per gram of dry stool.

4. Another aliquot of approximately 1 g of the homogenized specimen is placed in a sterile tube and weighed, and enough reduced 0.05% yeast extract solution is added to obtain a 10^{-1} dilution. From this dilution 10^{-2} to 10^{-9} dilutions are made in reduced 0.05% yeast extract solution. Two series are prepared.

   a) The first series is inoculated onto appropriate anaerobic media in the chamber, then removed from the chamber for inoculation of media for facultative and aerobic organisms. See Table A-1 for suggested media.

   b) The second series is heated at 80°C for 10 minutes and then is inoculated onto egg yolk agar for *Clostridium* and other heat-resistant species.

   c) Alternatively, one series of dilutions is prepared. One ml quantities are removed from each tube and placed into empty tubes which may be heated in a heating block within the chamber, or, a set of small tubes containing 1 ml ethanol is placed into the chamber and one ml is removed from each of the primary dilution tubes, mixed with the ethanol and allowed to stand for 30 to 45 minutes. The heated or ethanol-treated dilutions are plated on egg yolk agar for spore-forming organisms. The untreated dilutions are plated onto anaerobic and aerobic media.

5. Dilutions to be plated on the various media are indicated in Table A-1. Aside from the PRAS blood agar, which is poured in the chamber, all other media are poured on the bench (aerobic media can be purchased commercially) and brought into the chamber 24 hours prior to use. With a pipet, 0.1 ml of each dilution to be plated is spread over the medium indicated. This is done by the rotator-pipet method (6).

6. Plates are then placed in jars, sealed, removed from the chamber, and incubated for periods as indicated in Table A-1. If equipment permits, the plates may be incubated in the chamber.

7. If one wishes to culture for *Methanobacterium*, use the following procedure: An unheated set of dilutions in Hungate-type tubes is brought out of the chamber. PRAS tubes containing 4.9 ml of *Methanobacterium* medium are steamed to melt the agar. The tubes are placed in a 50°C water bath and 0.02 ml of 5% sodium sulfide, previously prepared by PRAS technique and autoclaved (this may be stored in the refrigerator for extended periods), is added to each tube just before inoculation. A syringe that is first gassed-out with oxygen-free CO_2 is used for this purpose and for subsequent inoculation of tubes with 0.1 ml of each of the dilutions to be cultured. After incubation for 1 to 2 weeks methane gas production is measured by analyzing the head-space gas.

8. Microscopic examinations

   a) A Gram stain is prepared from the 10^{-2} dilution. Twenty-five fields are counted.

   b) Petroff-Hausser chamber counts are made from the 10^{-3} dilution. Twenty-five fields are counted.

Table A-1 Procedures for anaerobic intestinal flora studies

Medium	Dilutions to be plated*		Days of incubation	Purpose
	Feces	Small bowel†		
Brucella PRAS blood agar	$10^{-7}, 10^{-8}, 10^{-9}$	$10^{-2}, 10^{-4}, 10^{-6}, 10^{-8}$	5-7	Total counts and predominant flora
Bacteroides bile esculin agar	$10^{-6}, 10^{-7}, 10^{-8}$	—	2-3	*B. fragilis* group
Kanamycin-vancomycin laked blood agar	$10^{-2}, 10^{-4}, 10^{-6}, 10^{-8}$	$10^{-2}, 10^{-4}, 10^{-6}, 10^{-8}$	3-5	Pigmented *Bacteroides*
Bifidobacterium medium	$10^{-4}, 10^{-6}, 10^{-7}, 10^{-8}$	$10^{-2}, 10^{-4}, 10^{-6}, 10^{-8}$	2-3	*Bifidobacterium*
Lactobacillus selective medium	$10^{-2}, 10^{-4}, 10^{-5}, 10^{-6}$	$10^{-2}, 10^{-4}, 10^{-6}$,	2-3	*Lactobacillus*
Rifampin blood agar	$10^{-4}, 10^{-6}, 10^{-8}$	—	2-3	*F. mortiferum/varium* and certain *Eubacterium* and *Clostridium* species
Cycloserine cefoxitin fructose agar	$10^{-2}, 10^{-4}, 10^{-6}, 10^{-8}$	—	2-3	*C. difficile*
Veillonella neomycin agar	$10^{-2}, 10^{-4}, 10^{-6}$	$10^{-2}, 10^{-4}, 10^{-6}$	2-3	*Veillonella* and other gram-negative cocci
Fusobacterium egg yolk agar	$10^{-2}, 10^{-4}, 10^{-6}$	$10^{-2}, 10^{-4}, 10^{-6}$	2-3	*Fusobacterium, Veillonella, Leptotrichia*
Egg yolk agar (heated or ethanol-treated dilutions)	$10^{-2}, 10^{-4}, 10^{-6}$	—	2-3	*Clostridium* sp.

* 0.1 ml of each dilution is placed on each medium used.

† Selective media optional. Direct examination of specimen indicates whether they may or may not be helpful.

c)   Darkfield examination is made as follows: Wet mount preparations are made by placing a small drop from the 10^{-2} and 10^{-3} dilutions on separate cover slips and placing the cover slips on microscopic slides. Preparations are surveyed at 500 x magnification and a detailed examination is made at 1500 x magnification. A minimum of 20 minutes should be spent in the examination.

9.   The dilutions are used for setting up aerobic cultures in a manner similar to that described for anaerobes. As a minimum, we recommend the following media: Brucella blood agar (as a nonselective medium), desoxycholate or MacConkey agar (for gram-negative bacilli), cetrimide agar (for *Pseudomonas*), mannitol salt agar (for *Staphylococcus*), Pfizer Selective *Enterococcus* agar (for group D streptococci), Sabouraud medium with chloramphenicol, 50 μg/ml, (for yeasts and fungi) [incubated at room temperature], and Mitis-Salivarius agar (for streptococci other than group D).

Identification of isolates

After appropriate incubation periods, colonies are counted and picked to a blood agar plate or other appropriate medium to obtain a pure culture. Aerotolerance testing and Gram stain are performed from the same colony. PRAS biochemicals and GLC are necessary to identify normal flora isolates. Total count is obtained by counting all colonies on the non-selective blood agar plate. The total count is multiplied by the wet/dry weight ratio and expressed as count/gram of stool, dry weight.

Alternatively, if species level of identification is not desired, characteristics such as Gram stain, disk identification reactions, growth on a specific selective medium, spore test, bile, and end-product analysis from a thioglycolate or chopped meat broth may give sufficient information to place an organism in a particular group (e.g., *Clostridium* sp., *B. fragilis* group, bile sensitive *Bacteroides* sp., anaerobic gram-positive cocci, etc.). We have used this abbreviated identification scheme when looking for gross effects of antimicrobial agents on fecal flora (114). We also stock all the strains so that further identification may be done later if desired.

Descriptions of typical colonies on selective anaerobe media

As with selective media for aerobes, selective media for anaerobes are not 100% inhibitory toward unwanted organisms; these may grow to a greater or lesser extent. Antibiotics in media, particularly cephalosporins, will deteriorate with time, especially if not stored in the refrigerator, thus allowing growth of unwanted organisms. If selective media are incubated for prolonged periods (>2 to 3 days), unwanted organisms may start to grow. In general, colonies 0.5 mm in diameter at 48 hours should not be picked unless the typical colony morphology of the organism is that size (e.g., *Veillonella* and some *Peptostreptococcus* sp.).

1.   Bacteroides-bile esculin agar (BBE)

Colonies of members of the *B. fragilis* group appear as gray-brown with brown to black halos. The one exception is *B. vulgatus*, which usually does not hydrolyze esculin and hence appears as light gray. This medium is highly selective, although occasionally yeast may grow; these appear as dry crinkly colonies and may be dark or gray in color. Also, a rare strain of *Pseudomonas* or an enteric may grow; their colony appearance is not predictable.

2. Kanamycin-vancomycin laked blood agar (KVLB)

Non-pigmented *Bacteroides* of all types grow on this medium and may be low convex or large and mucoid and vary in color from gray to yellow to tan to white. The pigmented *Bacteroides*, with the exception of *B. asaccharolyticus* and *B. gingivalis*, generally also grow on this medium. They may have a light tan color initially and become brown to black with prolonged incubation. *Fusobacterium* may occasionally grow on KVLB, especially in mixed culture. Occasional strains of enterics and yeast may also grow on this medium, but their colony morphology is not predictable. Since prolonged incubation may be desirable for pigment production, other organisms will probably grow.

3. Bifidobacterium medium (BIF)

Members of the genus *Bifidobacterium* appear as white mucoid, fairly large colonies. Because this medium is not highly selective, streptococci and lactobacilli also grow well and may have similar colony morphologies. Some strains of bifidobacteria grow poorly on blood agar and may have to be cultivated exclusively on this medium. Another medium described by Mitsuoka and others may be more selective (110).

4. Lactobacillus selective medium (LBS)

This is a highly selective medium for a few species of lactobacilli. They may appear as white to gray to yellow to orange in color, and are usually low convex and less than 2 to 3 mm in diameter. One should not assume that this medium will grow all lactobacilli.

5. Rifampin blood agar (RIF)

C. ramosum typically appears as a flat, grayish green, 2-3 mm diameter colony. Isolates of *Eubacterium* may have a similar appearance. *Fusobacterium varium* has a "fried egg" colony and *F. mortiferum* has low convex, tan, translucent colonies.

6. Cycloserine cefoxitin fructose agar (CCFA)

Colonies of *C. difficile* appear as large yellow colonies with an irregular edge. A few other species of *Clostridium* grow on this medium but appear more butyrous. The chartreuse fluorescence typical of *C. difficile* is best demonstrated on subculture to a blood agar plate, since the CCFA medium itself is fluorescent. This medium deteriorates rapidly if not refrigerated (39) and yeast, enterococci, and other enteric organisms will grow as small flat colonies.

7. Veillonella neomycin agar (VNA)

Veillonella appear as small transparent colonies. *Bacteroides* and *Fusobacterium* also grow on this medium and their appearance is similar to that on non-selective blood agar. Most gram-positive and many facultative gram negative rods are inhibited.

8. Fusobacterium egg yolk agar (FEA)

Colonies of *F. necrophorum* are lipase positive ("mother-of-pearl" sheen on and around them). Other *Fusobacterium* sp. are 1 to 3 mm, translucent to white, low convex to convex. *Veillonella* have 1 mm, translucent colonies. *Leptotrichia* forms 3 to 4 mm white, raised ground-glass appearing colonies. *Pseudomonas*, *Serratia*, *Providencia*, and *Proteus* are not significantly inhibited, although swarming by *P. mirabilis* is reduced.

9. Egg yolk agar (EYA)

The numerous species of clostridia have numerous different colony morphologies. *C. perfringens* is lecithinase positive (white precipitate around the colony). Other *Clostridium* species produce lipase which appears as a "mother-of-pearl" iridescence on and around the colony. Others may be both lipase and lecithinase negative and may not have distinctive colony morphology. It should be noted that for this medium to be selective for *Clostridium* sp., the dilution must first be ethanol or heat-treated to kill vegetative cells.

Oral flora

General techniques

Specimen collection

1. Plaque specimens. Specimens of supragingival or coronal plaque are collected with a scaler or currette and placed into a tube containing 5 ml of PRAS one-quarter strength Ringers solution.

Subgingival plaque samples are collected with a device which permits taking the sample from the most apical portion of the periodontal pocket (Fig. A-1). First, the supragingival plaque is removed, the gingival margin is retracted, then the cannula is inserted to the bottom of the pocket. Other details of the sampling procedure are given in the legend of Fig. A-1. The sample is introduced into a vial containing 0.3 ml of PRAS one-quarter strength Ringers solution with 0.1% sodium metaphosphate and processed as shown in Fig. A-2.

2. Saliva specimens. Stimulated or unstimulated saliva is collected in a sterile container, drawn into a syringe, then injected into an anaerobic specimen tube.

Processing of specimens

The directions given below are for subgingival plaque samples; these may be modified as necessary for other oral specimens.

1. The specimen is dispersed by sonication for 30 seconds (Fig. A-2) in an L & R T-14 ultrasonic cleaner (L & R Mfg. Co.).

2. All of the material from the vial is removed and all but enough to prepare slides for microscopic examination is injected into 5 ml PRAS one-quarter strength Ringers solution with 0.1% sodium metaphosphate.

3. Serial 10-fold dilutions are prepared in PRAS one-quarter strength Ringer solution without sodium metaphosphate and then plated on desired media. The amount of sample and density of bacteria in each sample varies, but

Fig. A-1.

Barb broach and wire
with calcium alginate fibers

Gas cannula

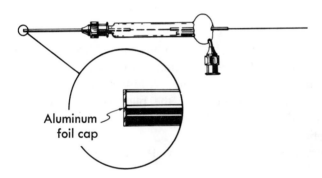

Aluminum
foil cap

a. The barbed broach is wound with calcium alginate fibers and inserted into a syringe with the plunger end modified to permit continuous flushing with oxygen-free gas. The tip of the needle is capped with aluminum foil and sterilized.

b. In use, the needle is placed into the sampling site, and the barbed broach is passed through the needle, dislodging the aluminum cap. The sample is taken and the broach drawn back into the needle, and the device removed from the site. The aluminum is removed by means of a scaler. (From Newman, M.G., and others: J. Periodont. 47:373-379, 1976. By permission of American Academy of Periodontology).

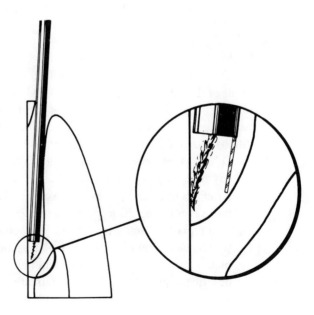

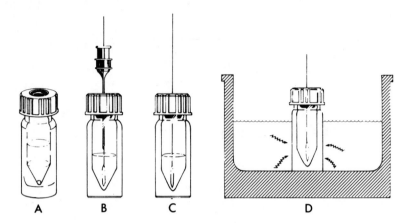

Fig. A-2. a. Screw capped vial with diaphragm. b. Broach containing sample inserted
through needle through the diaphragm. c. Needle removed from diaphragm
leaving broach inside. d. Sonicating sample prior to dilution.

samples usually contain 10^3 to 10^6 colony forming units. Material plated
from the 5 ml vial and the 10^{-1} through 10^{-4} dilutions will cover the range
of variation in the samples. A pipet is used to spread 0.1 ml of each dilution over the surface of the medium while the plate is being rotated.
Media to be used and conditions of incubation are indicated below.
  4. Microscopic examination
    a. A Gram stain is prepared from the initial vial containing the sample.
        All forms are described.
    b. A small drop of material from the initial sample vial is placed on a
        coverslip, ringed with vaseline, mounted on a slide, and then examined
        by dark-field microscopy. Microorganisms are described by shape and
        type of motility.

Specific Techniques
  Predominant flora (Table A-2)
    There is no one medium or environmental condition that will allow growth
  of all of the bacteria in oral samples. Many media have been used by different
  investigators. Some comparisons of media as well as environmental conditions
  have been made with conflicting results (103, 121,165). The media and conditions indicated below are those in use in many laboratories.
    1. Dilutions of specimens are plated on Brucella blood agar (or trypticase
       soy blood agar) and incubated anaerobically for 4 to 7 days.
    2. After incubation, plates are examined and total counts are made from
       those containing 30 to 300 colonies.
    3. From plates containing 30 to 100 colonies all colonies are described,
       picked and Gram stained. (If plates contain more than 100 colonies, the
       plate may be randomly divided in half and colonies from half the plate are
       described, picked, and Gram stained).

4. Replicate each colony to two blood agar plates and one chocolate agar plate. Streak one for anaerobic incubation and isolation. Leave the others as replicated spots in sectors of plates so that several colonies may be replicated on one plate. Incubate the blood plates anaerobically and in air, the chocolate plate in 10% CO_2 and air.
5. After 2 to 3 days incubation, proceed with identification of the isolates. Those which are anaerobic may be identified as described earlier. The microaerophiles and facultatives may be identified as described in the *Manual of Clinical Microbiology* (93) or *Diagnostic Microbiology* (47).

Selected flora (Table A-2)

Selective media or special procedures have been designed for isolation of specific groups of bacteria. They have the advantage of selecting out the bacteria desired, usually by inhibiting other groups of bacteria and allowing recovery of small numbers of the target bacteria in the presence of large numbers of others. They also may simplify identification procedures. However, selective media often have the disadvantage of inhibiting certain strains or species within the desired group.

Table A-2 Suggested media for oral flora studies.

Medium	Incubation Atmosphere/Period (days)		Purpose
Brucella blood agar (or trypticase soy blood agar)	Anaerobic	4-7	Total counts and predominant flora
Kanamycin-vancomycin laked blood agar (49)	Anaerobic	4-5	*B. melaninogenicus* and other *Bacteroides*
CVE (171)	Anaerobic	4-5	*Fusobacterium*
FEA (112)	Anaerobic	2	*Fusobacterium*
Veillonella agar (Rogosa)	Anaerobic	2	*Veillonella* and other gram negative cocci
Lactobacillus selective agar	Anaerobic	2	*Lactobacillus*
CFAT (186)	Air + 10% CO_2	4	*Actinomyces*
Brucella or trypticase soy blood agar	Air + 10% CO_2	2	Total counts and predominant capnophilic flora
Chocolate-bacitracin agar	Air + 10% CO_2	2	*Haemophilus, Campylobacter*, and other gram-negative capnophiles
Mitis-Salivarius agar	Air + 10% CO_2	2	Alpha and nonhemolytic streptococci

Bacteroides

1. Dilutions of the sample are plated as described above on kanamycin-vancomycin laked blood agar.
2. Plates are incubated anaerobically for 4 to 5 days. Appropriate colonies are enumerated, picked, Gram-stained and processed as described above.

Colonies of non-pigmented *Bacteroides* species are usually greyish, glistening, convex, or sometimes mucoid appearing. Brown to black colonies are usually one of the saccharolytic pigmented *Bacteroides* species. Most strains of the asaccharolytic species (*B. asaccharolyticus* and *B. gingivalis*) are inhibited by the vancomycin in this medium.

Fusobacterium nucleatum

1. Dilutions of the sample are plated as described above on crystal violet erythromycin blood agar (CVE) (171) or FEA (112).
2. Plates are incubated anaerobically for 4 to 5 days. Appropriate colonies are enumerated, picked, Gram-stained, and processed as described above.

Strains of *F. nucleatum* exhibit two types of colonies on CVE. One is a 2 mm transparent, smooth, round blue colony having an entire edge with a darker blue center. The other is a 1 to 2 mm transparent, round, or irregular blue colony with a speckled internal appearance.

Strains of *F. nucleatum* exhibit 1 to 3 mm, translucent to white, low convex to convex colonies on FEA.

Veillonella

1. Dilutions of the sample are plated on *Veillonella* agar with 7.5 μg vancomycin/ml.
2. Plates are incubated anaerobically for 2 to 3 days. Appropriate colonies are enumerated, picked, Gram stained, and processed as described previously. Colonies of *Veillonella* are approximately 1 mm in diameter, transparent, convex, with an entire edge.

Lactobacillus

1. Dilutions of the sample are plated on LBS agar.
2. Plates are incubated anaerobically for 4 days. Appropriate colonies are enumerated, picked and identified as described previously. Growth of some *Lactobacillus* strains (e.g., *L. acidophilus*) is reported to be enhanced by the addition of tomato juice.

Actinomyces

Several media have been described for selection of *A. viscosus* and *A. naeslundii*, (40, 89, 186). The medium (CFAT) developed by Zylber and Jordan (186) appears to permit uninhibited growth of human oral strains of the two species while inhibiting most of the other competing flora. Dilutions of samples are plated on CFAT medium, then incubated in 90% air and 10% CO_2 for 4 days.

Haemophilus and related bacteria

A chocolate-bacitracin agar described for isolation of *Haemophilus* from the respiratory tract (74) has been found useful for isolation of *Haemophilus*, *E. corrodens* and *A. actinomycetemcomitans* from the oral cavity (85).

Dilutions of samples are plated on this medium and incubated in 90% air and 10% CO_2 for 2 days. *Haemophilus* colonies are of 2 types: 1) a wrinkled greyish-white opaque type which can be slid intact across the surface of the agar, and 2) a smooth, buttery, low convex, greyish white, semitranslucent type. Both types vary in diameter from 0.5 to 2 mm.

Vaginal Flora

Although the role of anaerobes in "non-specific vaginitis" is uncertain, their presence in increased numbers, along with *Gardnerella vaginalis* and *Mobiluncus* sp., has been noted in women having this condition (126, 150, 151, 152). The following section describes techniques for quantitative cultures of vaginal fluid.

Collection and transport

Several methods have been described for collecting specimens for quantitative vaginal flora studies. Spiegel *et al.* (150) utilized a vaginal wash containing 3.5 ml sterile reduced saline containing 0.02% dithiothreitol (Sigma) and 0.0001% resazurin, in a 7 ml Red Top Vacutainer tube (B-D). Immediately before sample collection, the stopper is cleansed with alcohol and the reduced saline is removed with a syringe and injected through the speculum into the vagina. A swab is used to sweep the vaginal fluid into the saline pool, which is then reaspirated into the syringe; the air is expelled, and the saline is reinjected into the tube. Serial dilutions are prepared and plated onto appropriate media.

Bartlett *et al.* (15) utilized a two swab system. The first swab, stored in CO_2, is used to collect the sample, then immediately placed into prereduced Carey-Blair medium for culture. A second swab is stored in a tared screw cap tube. After sampling, it is returned to the tared tube and reweighed to estimate the amount of secretions obtained on the first swab. The swab for culture is brought into an anaerobic chamber and mixed vigorously until the swab has disintegrated and the Carey-Blair medium has liquefied. Serial dilutions are prepared and plated onto appropriate media.

Levison *et al.* (94) utilized a sterile 0.01 ml platinum loop to collect vaginal secretions through a speculum. The secretions were immediately diluted in prereduced brain heart infusion broth under the flow of oxygen-free gas. Serial dilutions were prepared and plated onto various media.

Table A-3 describes dilutions to be plated using the vaginal wash technique. The highest counts of organisms cultured by this technique are in the mid 10^9 range. Other sampling techniques may yield different total counts and dilution adjustments should be made accordingly.

Media listed in Table A-3 are those we have found to be most satisfactory. Use of the Rota-Plate (Fisher) is a convenient method to plate 0.1 ml quantities of each dilution onto the plates. The anaerobic plates may be incubated within the anaerobic chamber provided that adequate humidity is maintained. Alternatively, the plates may be placed into anaerobic jars with a fresh catalyst and removed from the chamber for incubation in a conventional incubator.

Table A-3 Suggested media for vaginal flora studies

Medium	Dilutions to be plated (0.1 ml)	Incubation Atmosphere	Period (days)	Purpose
Supplemented Brucella blood agar	$10^{-2}, 10^{-4}, 10^{-6}, 10^{-7}$	Anaerobic	3-6	Total count and predominant flora
Bacteroides bile esculin agar	$10^{-2}, 10^{-4}$	Anaerobic	2-3	B. fragilis group
Kanamycin-vancomycin laked blood agar	$10^{-2}, 10^{-4}, 10^{-6}, 10^{-7}$	Anaerobic	2-3	Bacteroides and pigmented Bacteroides*
Lactobacillus agar	$10^{-2}, 10^{-4}, 10^{-6}$	Anaerobic	2-3	Lactobacillus
Bifidobacterium agar	$10^{-2}, 10^{-4}, 10^{-6}$	Anaerobic	2-3	Lactobacillus and Bifidobacterium
Egg yolk agar (ethanol treated dilutions)	$10^{-2}, 10^{-4}$	Anaerobic	2-3	Clostridium
HV agar**	$10^{-2}, 10^{-4}, 10^{-6}, 10^{-7}$	Air + 10% CO_2	2-3	G. vaginalis
Chocolate agar	$10^{-2}, 10^{-4}, 10^{-6}, 10^{-7}$	Air + 10% CO_2	2-3	Total count, Haemophilus Neisseria
Thayer Martin	10^{-2}	Air + 10% CO_2	1-2	N. gonorrhoeae
Brucella blood agar	$10^{-2}, 10^{-4}, 10^{-6}, 10^{-7}$	Air + 10% CO_2	2-3	Total count
MacConkey agar	$10^{-2}, 10^{-4}$	Air	1-2	Enterics, Pseudomonas
PSE agar	$10^{-2}, 10^{-4}$	Air	1-2	Group D Streptococcus
Mannitol salt agar	$10^{-2}, 10^{-4}$	Air	1-2	Staphylococcus
Sabouraud agar	$10^{-2}, 10^{-4}$	Air	1-2	Yeasts and fungi

* Many strains of *B. asaccharolyticus* are inhibited by vancomycin at this concentration and will not grow on this medium.

** HBT agar (168) has also been shown to be a satisfactory medium for the recovery of *G. vaginalis* (HV and HBT are available from Remel).

The plates for aerobic incubation may be inoculated in the chamber along with the anaerobic plates and then removed or the dilutions may be removed from the chamber and plated on the bench.

For the egg yolk agar plate, 1 ml of each desired dilution is mixed with an equal volume of ethanol, allowed to stand for 30 to 45 minutes, and then plated in the same manner as the other plates. Since an additional 1:2 dilution has been made, the counts on this plate should be doubled.

Examining and processing of cultures

Examine plates incubated in the various atmospheres and count all or selected colony types on plates containing 30 to 300 colonies. Further processing is done as described for fecal isolates.

It should be noted that many strains of *B. asaccharolyticus* are susceptible to the concentration of vancomycin present in the KVLB plate; hence they may grow only on the Brucella blood agar plate and may require prolonged incubation to appear (at least 5 days). Additionally, some strains grow very poorly when isolation for pure culture is attempted.

B. ureolyticus may also be a slow grower. One should examine the blood agar plate for signs of a spreading-type of pitting, often adjacent to areas of heavy growth of other organisms. The colony itself may be very transparent and difficult to see.

G. vaginalis grows best on agar containing human blood and produces large zones of beta-hemolysis on human blood agars. However, it does grow slowly on other non-selective blood agars and may be picked from the anaerobic Brucella blood agar plate after prolonged incubation. Checking aerotolerance on blood or chocolate agar may give a false-negative result; it is therefore also advisable to check aerotolerance on human blood agar on isolates morphologically resembling *Gardnerella*.

Mobiluncus is a curved, motile, gram variable rod that has recently been described and appears to be associated with non-specific vaginitis (152).

STOCKING AND SHIPPING CULTURES
Stocking cultures

Stock cultures should be prepared as soon as an organism is isolated in pure culture. Isolates can be put into stock from liquid or solid media. In either case, the culture used should be young and actively growing.

Supplemented thioglycolate medium or chopped meat broth incubated for 24 to 48 hours, depending upon the growth rate of the isolate, can be used to prepare stock cultures. Add 0.5 ml of the liquid culture to an equal volume of sterile skim milk (20% powdered skim milk in distilled water) prepared in a screw-capped 1/2-dram vial. Freeze and maintain the stock culture at -70°C. Plate out a portion of the culture to check the purity of the isolate put into stock.

If stock cultures are prepared from solid media, the growth taken from the plate or slant must be suspended carefully and mixed thoroughly in the skim milk. An alternative suspending medium and a procedure for lyophilization are discussed in the *CDC Laboratory Manual* (34).

Shipping cultures

A small, sterile, stoppered serum vial containing a marble chip has proven to be a convenient shipping container. A few ml of a young culture in supplemented thioglycolate medium can be injected into the vial, which eliminates the need for a paraffin-plugged or paraffin-sealed tube and requires less space for shipping. If this is not practical, isolates can be shipped on chopped meat glucose slants or as stab cultures following adequate growth in *Brucella* agar deeps. Cultures may also be injected into commercially available transport vials.

Regulations concerning packaging and shipment of etiologic agents are detailed in NCCLS Tentative Standard TSH-5 (118).

MATERIALS AND METHODS †

Transport systems

The three tube-systems described below are recommended for transport of clinical specimens.

Agars (PRAS) - for transporting aspirates more than 2 ml in volume

    a.   Ingredients

Ionagar 2 (Oxoid)	2 g
Resazurin solution	0.4 ml
L-cysteine hydrochloride	0.05 g
Distilled water	100 ml

          20% sodium hydroxide

    b.   Preparation

       1) Combine all the ingredients except cysteine into a flask containing glass beads and boil until indicator is colorless.

       2) Gas with CO_2 as medium is cooling to 45°C.

       3) Add cysteine to warm medium.

       4) When cysteine has dissolved and the medium is still warm adjust the pH to 7.2 to 7.5 with 20% sodium hydroxide.

       5) Loosely cap the flask with a rubber stopper, pass into an anaerobic chamber*, and dispense 1.0 ml into disposable Hungate-type anaerobic culture tubes (Bellco).

       6) Screw the caps on tightly and remove from the chamber.

       7) Autoclave at 118°C (12 lbs) for 15 min.

       8) Store tubes at room temperature in the dark. (Resazurin is inactivated by light).

    c.   Shelf life

       One year or until indicator turns pink.

---

† Shelf life for materials is indicated where known. In other cases use quality control procedures to ensure reliable results.

* For an alternate method of dispensing PRAS media see VPI Manual (69).

Broth-PY medium (PRAS) - for transporting aspirates less than 2 ml in volume

   a.   Ingredients

Peptone	1 g
Yeast extract	1 g
Resazurin solution	0.4 ml
Distilled water	100 ml
L-cysteine hydrochloride	0.05 g
VPI salts solution	4 ml

       20% sodium hydroxide

   b.   Preparation

      1)   Combine all the ingredients except cysteine in a flask containing glass beads and boil until the indicator is colorless.

      2)   Gas with carbon dioxide while medium is cooling to 45°C.

      3)   Add cysteine.

      4)   When the cysteine has dissolved, adjust the pH to 6.8 with 20% sodium hydroxide.

      5)   Loosely cap the flask with a rubber stopper and immediately pass it into the chamber.

      6)   Dispense 1 ml into disposable Hungate-type anaerobic culture tubes (Bellco). Glass beads may be added to each tube to enhance mixing.

      7)   Screw the caps on tightly and remove from the chamber.

      8)   Autoclave at 118°C (12 lbs) for 15 minutes.

      9)   Store tubes at room temperature in the dark.

   c.   Shelf life

      One year or until indicator turns pink

Cary and Blair, modified (PRAS) - for transporting swab specimens.

   a.   Ingredients

Cary and Blair Medium (BBL)	2.5 g
Calcium chloride, 1% solution	1.8 ml
Resazurin solution	0.8 ml
L-cysteine hydrochloride	0.1 g
Distilled water	198 ml

       20% sodium hydroxide

   b.   Preparation

      1)   Combine all ingredients except cysteine into a flask containing glass beads.

      2)   Boil or steam until the agar is dissolved.

      3)   Gas with carbon dioxide while the medium is cooling to 45°C.

      4)   Add cysteine.

      5)   Gas with nitrogen.

      6)   When the cysteine is dissolved adjust the pH to 8.4 with 20% sodium hydroxide.

    7)   Loosely cap the flask with a rubber stopper, pass into an anaerobic chamber and dispense 10 ml into Hungate-type screw cap tubes or 16 × 125 mm roll tubes with butyl rubber stoppers.

    8)   Tightly cap or stopper the tubes and remove from the chamber.

    9)   Place butyl rubber stoppered tubes in a media press.

    10) Steam for 15 minutes on three consecutive days.

    11) Store tubes at room temperature in the dark.

  c. Shelf life

One year or until the indicator turns pink.

Anaerobic Swabs

  a. Place swabs in loosely capped Hungate tubes.

  b. Place these in an anaerobic chamber for 24 hours.

  c. Add 1 drop of distilled water to each tube

  d. Tighten caps and remove from chamber.

  e. Autoclave at 121°C for 15 minutes.

Culture Media

Most of the media suggested for use are available in dehydrated form and are prepared according to the directions of the manufacturer. Supplements are listed for each medium when enrichment is advisable or required. Most agar bases may be dispensed before autoclaving into screw capped tubes or 100 ml bottles and stored until needed. They can then be remelted, supplemented and poured into plates. Many prepared agar media are available from local media suppliers; PRAS blood agar, kanamycin-vancomycin laked blood agar, and phenylethyl alcohol agar plates are available from Anaerobe Systems.

Media used for biochemical tests and fermentation reactions are PRAS, are prepared as described in the VPI Anaerobe Laboratory Manual, and are supplemented with vitamin K_1 and hemin; they can be purchased from Scott Laboratories and Carr-Scarborough Microbiologicals, Inc. The use of thioglycolate-based medium recommended by CDC (34) (available from Scott Laboratories) is an acceptable alternative to the use of PRAS media (69); however, all reactions listed in this manual are based upon results obtained in PRAS media.)

Bacteroides bile esculin agar (BBE) (96)

  a. Ingredients

Trypticase soy agar	40 g
Oxgall	20 g
Esculin	1 g
Ferric ammonium citrate	0.5 g
Hemin solution (5 mg/ml)	2 ml
Gentamicin solution (40 mg/ml)	2.5 ml
Distilled water	1000 ml

  b. Preparation

    1)   Combine all the ingredients.

    2)   Adjust the pH to 7.0.

    3)   Boil or steam to dissolve.

    4)   Autoclave at 121°C for 15 minutes.

    5)   Cool to 50°C and pour plates.

  c. Shelf life

Plates - 2 weeks at room temperature

4 weeks at refrigerator temperature

Bottles- 1 year at refrigerator temperature

Bifidobacterium medium

  a. Ingredients

Canned tomato juice (Campbell's)	400 ml
Eugonagar (BBL)	45.5 g
Maltose	10 g
Hemin solution (5 mg/ml)	1 ml
Distilled water	600 ml

  b. Preparation

    1)   Combine all ingredients except the tomato juice in a flask.

    2)   Boil or steam to dissolve agar.

    3)   Add the tomato juice.

    4)   Autoclave at 118°C (12 lbs) for 15 minutes.

    5)   Cool to 50°C and pour plates. pH should be approximately 6.0.

  c. Shelf life

Plates - 1 week at room temperature.

Bottles - 1 year at refrigerator temperature.

Brucella Blood Agar

  a. Ingredients

Brucella agar (BBL)	43 g
Hemin solution (5 mg/ml)	1 ml
Vitamin K_1 solution (10 mg/ml)	1 ml
Distilled water	1000 ml
Sterile defibrinated sheep blood	50 ml

  b. Preparation

    1)   Combine all ingredients except sheep blood.

    2)   Boil to dissolve.

    3)   Autoclave at 121°C for 15 minutes.

    4)   Cool to 50°C, add sheep blood and pour plates.

  c. Shelf life

Plates - 2 weeks in refrigerator

Bottles - 1 year at refrigerator temperature

Brucella Broth

Brucella broth is used in broth dilution susceptibility tests.

  a. Ingredients

Brucella broth	28 g
Vitamin K_1 solution (1 mg/ml)	0.1 ml

  b. Preparation

    1)   Dissolve ingredients.

    2)   Dispense in convenient volumes.

    3)   Autoclave at 121°C for 15 minutes.
    4)   Add Fildes enrichment (5%, V/V) prior to use.
  c. Shelf life
    1 year at refrigerator temperature

Cadmium sulfate-fluoride-acridine Trypticase agar (CFAT) (186)
  a. Ingredients

Trypticase soy broth	30 g
Glucose	5 g
Agar	15 g
Cadmium sulfate	13 g
Sodium fluoride	80 g
Neutral acriflavin	1.20 mg
Basic fuchsin	0.25 mg
Distilled water	1000 ml
Sterile potassium tellurite	2.5 mg
Sterile defibrinated sheep blood	50 ml

  b. Preparation
    1)   Combine all ingredients except potassium tellurite and sheep blood.
    2)   Boil to dissolve.
    3)   Autoclave at 121°C for 15 minutes.
    4)   Cool to 50°C, add potassium tellurite and sheep blood, then pour plates.
  c. Shelf life - unknown

Chocolate-bacitracin agar (Modified from ref. 74)
  a. Ingredients

Blood agar base	40 g
Distilled water	1000 ml
Sterile defibrinated sheep blood	50 ml
Bacitracin	300 mg

  b. Preparation
    1)   Combine blood agar base and water.
    2)   Boil to dissolve.
    3)   Autoclave at 121°C for 15 minutes.
    4)   Cool to 50°C. Add blood.
    5)   Raise temperature to 70 to 80°C, mixing constantly but gently until blood turns a chocolate color.
    6)   Cool to 50°C, add bacitracin and pour plates.
  c. Shelf life
    Plates - 1 week at refrigerator temperature
    Bottles - 1 year at refrigerator temperature

Crystal violet erythromycin agar (CVE) (171)
  a. Ingredients

Trypticase	10 g
Yeast extract	5 g
Sodium chloride	5 g
Glucose	2 g

Tryptophane	0.2 g
Agar	15 g
Crystal violet	0.005 g
Distilled water	1000 ml
Sterile defibrinated sheep blood	50 ml
Erythromycin (dissolved in small volume of 95% ethanol)	4 mg

  b. Preparation
     1) Combine all ingredients except sheep blood and erythromycin.
     2) Adjust pH to 7.0 to 7.2.
     3) Autoclave at 121°C for 20 minutes.
     4) Cool to 50°C, add sheep blood and erythromycin, then pour plates.
  c. Shelf life
     Plates - 10 days at refrigerator temperature
     Bottles - 1 year at refrigerator temperature

Cycloserine-cefoxitin fructose agar (CCFA) (54)
  a. Ingredients

Proteose peptone No. 2	40 g
Disodium phosphate	5 g
Monopotassium phosphate	1 g
Fructose	6 g
Agar	20 g
Neutral Red (1% in ethanol)	3 ml
Distilled water	1000 ml
Cycloserine	500 mg
Cefoxitin	16 mg

  b. Preparation
     1) Combine all ingredients except cycloserine and cefoxitin.
     2) Adjust pH to 7.6.
     3) Boil to dissolve.
     4) Autoclave at 121°C for 15 minutes.
     5) Cool to 50°C, add cycloserine and cefoxitin, then pour plates.
  c. Shelf life
     Plates - 8 weeks at refrigerator temperature.
     Bottles - 1 year at refrigerator temperature

Egg yolk agar
  a. Ingredients

Proteose peptone No. 2	40 g
Disodium phosphate	5 g
Monopotassium phosphate	1 g
Sodium chloride	2 g
Magnesium sulfate	0.1 g
Glucose	2 g
Hemin solution (5 mg/ml)	1 ml

Agar	20 g
Distilled water	1000 ml
Egg yolk emulsion (Difco or laboratory preparation)	50 ml
or Egg yolk emulsion (Oxoid)	74 ml

b. Preparation
1) Combine all ingredients except egg yolk.
2) Adjust pH to 7.6.
3) Boil to dissolve.
4) Autoclave at 121°C for 15 minutes.
5) Cool to 50°C; add egg yolk emulsion and pour plates.

c. Shelf life
Plates - 1 week at refrigerator temperature
Bottles - 1 year at refrigerator temperature

Fusobacterium egg yolk agar (FEA) (112)

a. Ingredients

Brucella agar base	37 g
Disodium phosphate	5 g
Monopotassium phosphate	1 g
Magnesium sulfate	0.1 g
Hemin solution (5 mg/ml)	1 ml
Polysorbate 80	1 ml
Neomycin solution (100 mg/ml)	1 ml
Distilled water	1000 ml
Vancomycin solution (7.5 mg/ml)	0.67 ml
Josamycin (Yamanouchi Pharmaceuticals)	3 mg
Egg yolk emulsion (Difco or laboratory preparation)	50 ml
or Egg yolk emulsion (Oxoid)	74 ml

b. Preparation
1) Combine all ingredients except egg yolk emulsion, vancomycin and josamycin.
2) Adjust pH to 7.6.
3) Boil to dissolve.
4) Autoclave at 121°C for 15 minutes.
5) Cool to 50°C, add egg yolk emulsion, vancomycin and josamycin, then pour plates.

c. Shelf life
Plates - 1 week at refrigerator temperature
Bottles - 1 year at refrigerator temperature

Kanamycin-vancomycin laked blood agar

a. Ingredients

Brucella agar (BBL)	43 g
Hemin solution (5 mg/ml)	1 ml

Vitamin K$_1$ solution (10 mg/ml)	1 ml
Kanamycin solution (100 mg/ml)	0.75 ml
Distilled water	1000 ml
Vancomycin solution (7.5 mg/ml)	1 ml
Laked sheep blood	50 ml

  b. Preparation
1) Combine all ingredients except vancomycin and laked sheep blood.
2) Boil to dissolve.
3) Autoclave at 121°C for 15 minutes.
4) Cool to 50°C, add vancomycin and laked sheep blood (blood frozen overnight then thawed), then pour plates.

  c. Shelf life
Plates - 1 week at refrigerator temperature
Bottles - 1 year at refrigerator temperature

Lactobacillus selective medium (LBS)

  a. Ingredients

LBS agar (Rogosa-BBL)	8.4 g
Tomato juice	40 ml
Distilled water	60 ml
Acetic acid (glacial)	0.13 ml

  b. Preparation
1) Mix ingredients.
2) Steam for 20 to 30 minutes until agar dissolves or heat with frequent agitation and boil for 1 minute. *Do not autoclave.*
3) Cool to 45°C and pour plates.

  c. Shelf life
Plates - 24 hours at room temperature

Methanobacterium medium (PRAS)

  a. Ingredients

Rumen fluid	15 ml
Sodium chloride	0.2 g
Ammonium chloride	0.1 g
Monopotassium phosphate	0.1 g
Magnesium chloride, 6-hydrate	0.1 g
Calcium chloride	0.1 g
Ammonium molybdate, 4-hydrate	0.002 g
Cobalt chloride, 6-hydrate	0.002 g
Sodium bicarbonate	0.4 g
Resazurin solution	0.8 ml
L-cysteine hydrochloride	0.05 g
Distilled water	200 ml

  b. Preparation
1) Combine all ingredients except cysteine.
2) Steam for 15 minutes (resazurin will stay pink).

3) Cool while gassing with CO_2.
4) Add cysteine, dissolve, adjust pH to 6.8. At this time, indicator will be colorless.
5) Switch from CO_2 to 70% H_2 and 30% CO_2 (*explosive mixture*).
6) Place 0.125 g agar in each roll tube.
7) Dispense in 4.9 ml amounts, gassing with 70% H_2 and 30% CO_2.
8) Autoclave tubes in a media press at 121°C for 15 minutes.
9) Just before use, add 0.02 ml of sterile 5% Na_2S solution
   c. Shelf life - 3 months at room temperature.

Phenylethyl alcohol blood agar (PEA)
  a. Ingredients

Phenylethyl alcohol agar	42.5 g
Vitamin K_1 solution (10 mg/ml)	1 ml
Distilled water	1000 ml
Sterile defibrinated sheep blood	50 ml

  b. Preparation
1) Combine ingredients except sheep blood.
2) Boil to dissolve.
3) Autoclave at 121°C for 15 minutes.
4) Cool to 50°C, add sheep blood, then pour plates.
  c. Shelf life
  Plates - 2 weeks at refrigerator temperature
  Bottles - 1 year at refrigerator temperature

Rifampin Blood Agar (160)
  a. Ingredients

Brucella agar (BBL)	43 g
Hemin solution (5 mg/ml)	1 ml
Vitamin K_1 solution (10 mg/ml)	1 ml
Distilled water	1000 ml
Sterile defibrinated sheep blood	50 ml
Rifampin solution (1000 μg/ml)	50 ml

  b. Preparation
1) Combine all ingredients except sheep blood and rifampin.
2) Boil to dissolve.
3) Autoclave at 121°C for 15 minutes.
4) Cool to 50°C, add rifampin and sheep blood, then pour plates.
  c. Shelf life
  Plates - 1 week at refrigerator temperature
  Bottles - 1 year at refrigerator temperature

Thioglycolate, supplemented
  a. Ingredients

Thioglycollate medium without indicator BBL - 135C	30 g
Hemin solution (5 mg/ml)	1 ml

Vitamin K$_1$ (1 mg/ml)	0.1 ml
Distilled water	1000 ml

  b. Preparation
     1) Combine ingredients.
     2) Boil to dissolve.
     3) Dispense in tubes containing a marble chip (Fisher), filling the tubes two-thirds to three-fourths full.
     4) Autoclave at 118°C to 121°C for 15 minutes.
  c. Use
     1) Just prior to use boil or steam for 5 minutes, cool.
     2) Supplement with normal rabbit or horse serum (10%) or Fildes enrichment (5%).
  d. Shelf life - 2 weeks at room temperature

Veillonella-neomycin agar
  a. Ingredients

Veillonella agar	36 g
Neomycin solution (100 mg/ml)	1 ml
Distilled water	1000 ml
Vancomycin solution (7.5 mg/ml)	1 ml

  b. Preparation
     1) Combine all ingredients except vancomycin.
     2) Boil to dissolve.
     3) Autoclave at 121°C for 15 minutes.
     4) Cool to 50°C, add vancomycin and pour plates.
  c. Shelf life
     Plates - 1 week at refrigerator temperature
     Bottles - 1 year at refrigerator temperature

Wilkins - Chalgren agar
  a. Ingredients

Trypticase	10 g
Gelysate	10 g
Yeast extract	5 g
Dextrose	1 g
Sodium chloride	5 g
L-arginine-free base	1 g
Sodium pyruvate	1 g
Vitamin K$_1$	0.5 mg
Hemin	5 mg
Agar	15 g
Distilled water	1000 ml

  b. Preparation
     1) Combine ingredients.
     2) Boil to dissolve.
     3) Dispense into screw cap tubes.

      4)   Autoclave at 121°C for 15 minutes.

  c. Shelf life - 4 weeks at refrigerator temperature

Reagents and Diluents

Antitoxin - C. perfringens type A

Available from Wellcome Animal Health (for use in the Nagler test).

Arginine (10%)

  a. Ingredients

      Arginine HC1   10 g

      Distilled water   100 ml

  b. Preparation

      1)   Dissolve the arginine HC1 in water.

      2)   Sterilize by filtration.

      3)   Store in the refrigerator.

  c. Use

      Add 0.5 ml to 10 ml of freshly steamed thioglycolate medium for growth stimulation of *E. lentum*.

Egg Yolk Emulsion

  a. Ingredients

      Fresh eggs

      Sterile normal saline

  b. Preparation

      1)   Cleanse fresh eggs thoroughly with an alcohol pad.

      2)   Punch an airhole in one end and a hole approximately 10 mm in diameter in the other end.

      3)   Carefully allow the white to drip out, assisting as necessary with sterile syringe and needle.

      4)   When white has been removed, aspirate yolk into a sterile syringe.

      5)   Place in sterile flask with glass beads and an equal volume of normal saline.

      6)   Mix thoroughly and test sterility by plating a drop on Brucella blood agar and inoculating 1 ml into supplemented thioglycolate medium.

         Prepared egg yolk emulsion is available from Difco and Oxoid.

Ehrlich reagent

  a. Ingredients

      Para-dimethylaminobenzaldehyde   1 g

      Ethyl alcohol (95%)   95 ml

      Hydrochloric acid (concentrated)   20 ml

  b. Preparation

      1)   Dissolve para-dimethylaminobenzaldehyde in alcohol.

      2)   Slowly add hydrochloric acid.

      3)   Store in a dark bottle and refrigerate.

Ferric ammonium citrate (1%)

  a. Ingredients

Ferric ammonium citrate	1 g
Distilled water	100 ml

   b.   Preparation
      1)   Dissolve ferric ammonium citrate in water.
      2)   Store in a dark bottle and refrigerate.

Fildes Enrichment

Available from BBL and Difco

Formate-fumarate additive

   a.   Ingredients

Sodium formate	3 g
Fumaric acid	3 g
Distilled water	50 ml
Sodium hydroxide	20 pellets

   b.   Preparation
      1)   Combine ingredients, stirring until pellets are dissolved and fumaric acid is in solution.
      2)   Bring pH to 7.0 with 4N sodium hydroxide.
      3)   Sterilize by filtration.
   c.   Use
      Add 0.5 ml to 10 ml of culture medium to stimulate growth of *B. ureolyticus* and other fastidious gram-negatives.

Hemin solution (5 mg/ml)

   a.   Ingredients

Hemin	0.5 g
Commercial ammonia water or sodium hydroxide (1N)	10 ml
Distilled water	90 ml

   b.   Preparation
      1)   Dissolve hemin in ammonia water or sodium hydroxide (1N). Bring volume to 100 ml.
      2)   Autoclave at 121°C for 15 minutes.
   c.   Use
      Add to medium as a supplement in a final concentration of 5μg/ml.

Kanamycin solution (100 mg/ml)

   a.   Ingredients

Kanamycin	1 g
Sterile phosphate buffer, pH8,	10 ml

   b.   Preparation
      1)   Dissolve kanamycin in phosphate buffer.
      2)   Store in refrigerator for up to 1 year.

McFarland standard

   a.   Ingredients
      Barium chloride, 1% aqueous
      Sulfuric acid, 1% aqueous

Table A-4 Preparation of McFarland nephelometer standards.

Tube No.	1% barium chloride (ml)	1% sulfuric acid (ml)	Corresponding approximate density of bacteria/ml
1	0.1	9.9	3×10^8
2	0.2	9.8	6×10^8
3	0.3	9.7	9×10^8
4	0.4	9.6	1.2×10^9
5	0.5	9.5	1.5×10^9
6	0.6	9.4	1.8×10^9
7	0.7	9.3	2.1×10^9
8	0.8	9.2	2.4×10^9
9	0.9	9.1	2.7×10^9
10	1.0	9.0	3×10^9

    b. Preparation
       1) Add amounts of the two solutions indicated in table A-4 to tubes or ampules
       2) Seal
Note: Tubes or ampules should have the same diameter as the tube to be used in subsequent density determinations.

0.5 McFarland standard
    a. Ingredients
          Barium chloride, 1% aqueous   0.5 ml
          Sulfuric acid 1% aqueous   99.5 ml
    b. Preparation
       1) Mix the two solutions.
       2) Vortex and immediately dispense into an appropriate tube or ampule and seal.
Note: the tube or ampule should have the same diameter as the tube to which it will be compared. Unless the standard is contained in a heat-sealed tube or ampule it should be replaced every 6 months.

Neomycin solution (100 mg/ml)
    a. Ingredients
          Neomycin   1 g
          Sterile phosphate buffer, pH8   10 ml
    b. Preparation
       1) Dissolve neomycin in phosphate buffer.
       2) Store in refrigerator for up to 1 year.

Nessler reagent
    a. Ingredients
          Mercuric iodide   100 g

Potassium iodide	70 g
Distilled water	
Sodium hydroxide (8N)	500 ml

Preparation
1) Dissolve mercuric iodide and potassium iodide in 100 to 200 ml distilled water.
2) Add this solution slowly and with stirring to the 8N sodium hydroxide at 20 to 25°C.
3) Adjust volume to 1 liter with distilled water.
4) Store in a rubber stoppered bottle in the dark for up to 1 year.

Nitrate disks (178)
  a. Ingredients

Potassium nitrate	30 g
Sodium molybdate dihydrate	0.1 g
Distilled water	100 ml
Sterile 1/4 inch filter paper disks	

  b. Preparation
1) Dissolve the nitrate and molybdate in the water.
2) Sterilize by filtration.
3) Dispense 20 μl quantities of the solution onto the disks.
4) Allow the disks to dry at room temperature for 72 hours.

Nitrate Reagents
  a. Ingredients
    1) Solution A

Sulfanilic acid	0.5 g
Glacial acetic acid	30 ml
Distilled water	120 ml

    2) Solution B

1,6-Cleve's acid	0.2 g
Glacial acetic acid	30 g
Distilled water	120 ml

  b. Preparation
Dissolve ingredients of each solution in distilled water in separate containers.

Oxgall (40%)
  a. Ingredients

Oxgall	40 g
Distilled water	100 ml

  b. Preparation
1) Dissolve oxgall in water.
2) Autoclave at 121°C for 15 minutes.
3) Store in refrigerator.
  c. Use
Add 0.5 ml to 10 ml of thioglycolate medium.

Paradimethylaminocinnamaldehyde (1%) (158)
  a. Ingredients
        Paradimethylaminocinnamaldehyde (Aldrich)   1 g
        Hydrochloric acid (10%)   100 ml
  b. Preparation
        1) Dissolve paradimethylaminocinnamaldehyde in the hydrochloric acid
              solution.
        2) Store in a dark bottle in refrigerator.

Resazurin
  a. Ingredients
        Resazurin (Allied Chemical # 506)   1 tablet
        Distilled water   44 ml
  b. Preparation
        Dissolve tablet in water.
        Store at room temperature.

Rifampin (1 mg/ml)
  a. Ingredients
        Rifampin   100 mg
        Absolute ethanol   20 ml
        Distilled water   80 ml
  b. Preparation
        1) Dissolve rifampin in the alcohol.
        2) Add the distilled water.
        3) Store in refrigerator for up to 2 months.

Ringer solution
  a. Ingredients
        Sodium chloride   9 g
        Calcium chloride, dihydrate   0.25 g
        Potassium chloride   0.4 g
        Distilled water   1000 ml
  b. Preparation
        1) Combine all ingredients.
        2) Mix to dissolve.

One-quarter strength Ringer solution with metaphosphate
  a. Ingredients
        Ringer solution   50 ml
        Resazurin solution   0.8 ml
        Distilled water   150 ml
        Sodium metaphosphate   0.2 g
        L-cysteine hydrochloride   0.1 g
  b. Preparation
        1) Combine all ingredients.
        2) Mix to dissolve, dispense.
        3) Autoclave at 121°C for 15 minutes.

Ringer dilution solution
  a. Ingredients

Ringer solution	200 ml
Resazurin solution	0.8 ml
L-cysteine hydrochloride	0.1 g

  b. Preparation
    1) Combine all ingredients.
    2) Mix to dissolve, dispense 9 ml into disposable Hungate anaerobic culture tubes (Bellco).
    3) Autoclave at 121°C for 15 minutes.

Sodium bicarbonate (20 mg/ml)
  a. Ingredients

Sodium bicarbonate	2 g
Distilled water	100 ml

  b. Preparation
    1) Dissolve sodium bicarbonate in water.
    2) Sterilize by filtration.
    3) Store in refrigerator.
  c. Use
    Add 0.5 ml to 10 ml of medium.

Sodium polyanethol sulfonate (SPS) disks (179)
  a. Ingredients

Sodium polyanethol sulfonate (Harleco)	5 g
Distilled water	100 ml
Sterile 1/4 inch filter paper disks	

  b. Preparation
    1) Dissolve sodium polyanethol sulfonate in water.
    2) Sterilize by filtration.
    3) Dispense 20 μl onto each filter paper disk.
    4) Allow to dry at room temperature for 72 hours.
    5) Store at room temperature for up to 6 months.
    (Disks are available from Anaerobe Systems, Remel and Scott Laboratories, Inc.)

Tween-80®
  a. Ingredients

Tween-80®	10 ml
Distilled water	90 ml

  b. Preparation
    1) Mix ingredients.
    2) Autoclave at 121°C for 15 minutes.
  c. Use
    Add 0.5 ml to thioglycolate medium to enhance growth of most gram-positive bacteria.

Urea broth
 a. Ingredients
  Urea broth (Difco)   38.7 g
  Distilled water   1000 ml
 b. Preparation
  1) Combine ingredients.
  2) Sterilize by filtration.
  3) Dispense into sterile screw capped tubes.

Vancomycin stock solution (7.5 mg/ml)
 a. Ingredients
  Vancomycin   75 mg
  Hydrochloric acid (N/20)   5 ml
  Distilled water   5 ml
 b. Preparation
  1) Dissolve vancomycin in hydrochloric acid.
  2) Add distilled water.
  3) Store in refrigerator for up to 1 month or in freezer (-20°C) for up to
      1 year.

Vitamin K₁ solution (10 mg/ml)
 a. Ingredients
  Vitamin K$_1$ (Nutritional Biochemical Corp.)   0.2 g
  Absolute ethanol   20 ml
 b. Preparation
  1) Weigh out the vitamin K$_1$ on a small piece of sterile aluminum foil.
  2) Add this, aseptically, to a tube or bottle containing the ethanol.
  3) Store in refrigerator in tightly closed container, protected from light.
  4) Dilutions of this solution may be made in distilled water.
 c. Use
  1) To supplement liquid media, add to a final concentration of 0.1 µg/ml.
  2) To supplement solid media, add to a final concentration of 10 µg/ml.

VPI salts solution (69)
 a. Ingredients
  Calcium chloride (anhydrous)   0.2 g
  Magnesium sulfate (anhydrous)   0.2 g
  Dipotassium phosphate   1 g
  Monopotassium phosphate   1 g
  Sodium bicarbonate   10 g
  Sodium chloride   2 g
  Distilled water   1000 ml
 b. Preparation
  1) Mix calcium chloride and magnesium sulfate in 300 ml water until
      dissolved.
  2) Add 500 ml water and while stirring add remaining salts.
  3) Continue stirring until all salts are dissolved.
  4) Add 200 ml water, mix.
  5) Store in refrigerator.

Biochemical tests and miscellaneous procedures

Ammonia production

See nitrate and urease tests.

Bile

Inoculate a tube of PRAS PYG containing 2% commercial dehydrated oxgall (equivalent to 20% bile) and 0.1% sodium deoxycholate, as well as a control tube of PRAS PYG. Incubate and compare growth in the two tubes. Record as inhibition (less growth than in control; not necessarily total inhibition), no inhibition, or enhancement of growth. An alternative to the use of PRAS media is thioglycolate. Inoculate a tube of thioglycolate medium with 20% bile and 0.1% sodium deoxycholate and a tube of thioglycolate medium without bile or deoxycholate. Incubate and observe as above.

If BBE agar is used for determination of growth inhibition by bile, the incubated medium should be observed for the presence of growth of the bacteria, not just hydrolysis of esculin.

Bile disks (15 mg) are available from Remel. Place disk on heavily streaked area of BAP. After 24-48 h incubation a zone of inhibition denotes bile sensitivity (66,174).

Catalase

Drop 3% hydrogen peroxide on growth on egg yolk agar (or other medium that does not contain blood) and observe for evolution of bubbles. Alternatively, growth may be removed from this medium or blood agar to a drop of hydrogen peroxide on a glass slide and observed for evolution of bubbles. Another method utilizes 15% hydrogen peroxide and appears to be somewhat more sensitive.

Disk identification (159)

If disk identification is not done on the purity plate as outlined in Chapter 3, a subculture may be used. Use an actively growing culture in supplemented thioglycolate medium as an inoculum source. Moisten a swab and distribute the inoculum evenly over the surface of a Brucella blood agar plate. Use the following disks; colistin, 10 μg; kanamycin, 1000 μg; vancomycin, 5 μg; and a nitrate disk. If the organism is a gram-positive coccus or coccobacillus also include an SPS disk. Incubate anaerobically for 48 h. Measure and record zones of inhibition. For antibiotics, zones less than 10 mm = resistant; equal to or greater than 10 mm = sensitive. For SPS, zones greater than 12 mm = sensitive; a hazy zone is considered resistant. Test nitrate disk for reduction of nitrate.

Esculin hydrolysis

Inoculate a tube of peptone yeast esculin broth and, after good growth is obtained, add a few drops of 1% ferric ammonium citrate solution. A positive reaction is indicated by its turning black. Alternatively, the tube may be observed under long wave ultraviolet light (365 nm). Loss of fluorescence indicates a positive reaction. Qadri and co-workers have described a rapid test (130).

Fermentation of carbohydrates

Tubes of peptone yeast (PY) broth containing various carbohydrates are inoculated. After good growth is obtained, pH is determined using a pH meter equipped with a long thin electrode. Interpretation is as follows: below pH 5.5

= acid, 5.5-6.0 = weak acid, and above 6.0 = negative. For *Bacteroides* sp. fermenting glucose, a pH higher than 5.7 is considered negative. Uninoculated tubes from each batch of medium should be gassed with CO_2 and incubated along with the inoculated tubes. Ordinarily the pH of such gassed uninoculated tubes will be 6.2 to 6.4. Occasionally, carbohydrate broths such as arabinose and xylose will have a pH of 5.8 or 5.9.

Gelatin liquefaction

Test after good growth is observed by refrigerating an inoculated gelatin tube along with an uninoculated tube until the latter tube has solidified (usually 1/2 to 1 hour). Remove tubes to room temperature and invert. A positive reaction is indicated if the inoculated tube fails to solidify. A weak reaction is indicated when the inoculated tube begins to become liquid at the time the tube comes to room temperature.

Growth tests

The growth of some anaerobic isolates is enhanced by the addition of supplements, for example, arginine, Fildes enrichment, formate-fumarate, pyruvate, serum or Tween 80. If an isolate fails to grow well in PRAS PYG, supplements should be added, using PYG as the base medium. After a 48- to 72-h incubation, growth in the tubes containing supplements is compared with growth in PYG. If one of the supplements enhances growth, it should be added to each tube required for biochemical tests before inoculation. The same growth test principle can be applied if thioglycolate medium is used as the base for determining fermentation and biochemical reactions.

Indole production

Spot test (158). Remove a loopful of growth from a pure culture on a blood agar plate, which must contain tryptophane. Do not test different isolates picked from the same culture plate; this can cause false-positive reactions because indole is a diffusible product. Smear the growth on filter paper that has been saturated with 1% paradimethylaminocinnamaldehyde in 10% (V/V) concentrated hydrochloric acid. A positive reaction is indicated by the rapid development of blue color around the growth. Dark pigmented *Bacteroides* may give a greenish color. Negative reactions give no color change or a pinkish color. Late color development should be disregarded.

Tube test. Remove approximately 2.0 ml of culture from indole-nitrite medium or chopped meat broth and put into a tube for testing. Add 1.0 ml of xylene, shake well, and let stand at least 2 minutes. Slowly add 0.5 ml of Ehrlich reagent down the side of the tube. Development of a pink or fuchsia ring within 10 to 15 minutes is a positive reaction; a yellow ring is negative.

NOTE: One report (146) has indicated that false-negative indole tests may be obtained with certain facultative bacteria in indole-nitrite medium when nitrite concentrations reach 0.25 to 0.75 mg/ml. This problem has not been investigated with the anaerobic bacteria. We have used indole-nitrite medium for several years and have had a number of strains that reduce nitrate to nitrite and at the same time give positive indole tests. However, more reliable results might be obtained by the use of a medium that does not contain nitrate prepared with a peptone rich in tryptophane such as trypticase or tryptone. Also, false-positive results have been obtained with some batches of PRAS chopped meat medium, especially after prolonged storage (personal communication, W.E.C. Moore).

Lactate conversion to propionate

Chromatograph lactate and PY culture doing only volatile fatty acid determination (aqueous or ether extract), and compare the amounts of propionic acid produced. If more propionic acid is detected in lactate than in PY, lactate has been converted. Chopped meat medium contains sufficient lactate to permit its use for this purpose.

Lecithinase

A positive lecithinase reaction on egg yolk agar is indicated by an opaque zone in the medium around the colonies.

Lipase

A positive lipase reaction on egg yolk agar is indicated by an iridescent sheen on the surface of the growth (observed under oblique light). This reaction may be delayed. Therefore, plates should be kept 1 week before being discarded as negative.

Meat digestion

Test is performed in chopped meat medium. A positive reaction is indicated by disintegration and gradual disappearance of meat particles, leaving a flocculent sediment in the tube. Digestion may require 14 to 21 days.

Milk

Observe for development of clot in 2 to 4 days. Observe for gas and digestion for up to 3 weeks. The tube will gradually become clear as digestion takes place. This may occur with or without clot formation. Determine pH at the end of the incubation period. If strongly acid, digestion has not occurred.

Nagler reaction

Prior to inoculating an egg yolk agar plate, swab one-half of the plate with *C. perfringens* type A antitoxin and allow it to dry. Streak the inoculum across both halves of the plate, starting on the half without antitoxin. Incubate 24 to 48 hours and observe. Inhibition of lecithinase production on the half of the plate containing the antitoxin indicates a positive reaction. This antitoxin is not specific for *C. perfringens*. Other species that will also give a positive Nagler reaction are *C. bifermentans*, *C. sordellii*, and *C. barati*.

Nitrate reduction

Put 1.0 ml of test culture from indole-nitrite medium (BBL) into separate tube. Add 2.0 ml nitrate reagent A and 0.2 ml nitrate reagent B. If using nitrate discs, remove disc from surface of plate and place in a clean Petri dish. Add 1 drop each of reagents A and B. Development of pink to red color indicates nitrate has been reduced to nitrite. If no color develops in a few minutes, add a small amount of zinc dust and wait 5 minutes. Development of red color indicates that nitrate was not reduced. If no color develops, nitrate was reduced beyond nitrite (positive test), and the remaining portion of the indole-nitrite culture should be tested for ammonia by adding a few drops of Nessler reagent. A deep orange color indicates a positive reaction. The disk cannot be tested for ammonia.

Reverse Camp Test (24,65)

Inoculate a BA with a single streak of suspected *C. perfringens*. Then inoculate a group B beta hemolytic *Streptococcus* in a single streak at a 90 angle to within a few mm of the *Clostridium*. (More than one test can be inoculated on each plate). Incubate anaerobically for 24 to 48 h. Examine for an arrowhead of synergistic hemolysis.

Spores

Spores can be observed in stained preparations (Gram or spore stain) made from solid or broth medium. Some commonly encountered species (such as *C. perfringens* and *C. ramosum*) sporulate poorly, and spores are rarely seen. Heat tests are often used if spores cannot be demonstrated in stained smear. Growth from chopped meat slant or other solid medium should be suspended in two tubes of starch broth, and care should be taken not to touch loop to sides of tubes above the level of the medium; at the same time, subculture to BAP for anaerobic incubation to check viability. Place one tube of starch broth in a water bath at 70°C, with water level above the level of the medium in the tube. Place tube containing an equal amount of water and thermometer in water bath at the same time. Leave starch tube in bath for 10 minutes after tube of water has reached 70°C. Remove starch tube and incubate with the unheated tube. Observe for growth (up to 5 days). Growth in both tubes indicates a positive test. If growth is questionable on visual inspection, both tubes should be subcultured.

An alternative method is to mix equal volumes of a 1-week-old thioglycolate or chopped meat broth culture with 95% ethanol. Mix gently and allow to remain at room temperature for 30 minutes. Subculture to BA, incubate anaerobically for 2 days, and examine for growth (88).

Starch hydrolysis

Add a few drops of Gram's iodine to culture in starch broth. Observe immediately. If no color is seen, starch has been hydrolyzed. If blue-black color is seen, starch is still present and the reaction is recorded as negative. This color disappears rapidly, but the initial blue-black color is still an indication that starch is present.

Threonine conversion to propionate

Chromatograph threonine and PY culture doing only a volatile fatty acid determination (aqueous or ether extract), and compare the amounts of propionic acid produced. If more propionic acid is detected in threonine than PY, threonine has been converted.

Urease

Scrape growth from egg yolk agar or other solid medium. Make a heavy suspension in 0.5 ml of sterile urea broth. Incubate and observe for up to 24 hours aerobically. A bright red color indicates a positive reaction. With a heavy inoculum, urease production usually is evident within 15 to 30 minutes. If indicator has been reduced, add Nessler reagent to determine ammonia production. Presence of ammonia indicates a positive reaction.

QUALITY CONTROL PROCEDURES

All media, reagents and test systems should be tested periodically for their ability to perform as effectively and accurately as possible. Quality control procedures for gas-liquid chromatography and antimicrobial susceptibility testing have been described in chapters 4 and 5. Where tests such as the gram stain are common to aerobic, facultative and anaerobic bacteria, results obtained for the aerobic or facultative bacteria will suffice.

All anaerobic systems should be tested daily for anaerobiosis using an indicator such as resazurin or methylene blue. When using resazurin, it must be protected from light to prevent inactivation. If the methylene blue strip is not white upon opening the foil packet, discard and use a fresh one.

Quality control procedures suggested for commonly used anaerobic media and reagents are given in Tables A-5 and A-6. When testing other media such as FEA for example, the procedure should be designed to show that small numbers of *F. necrophorum* can grow and produce lipase while gram-positive cocci and most *Bacteroides* are inhibited or will not grow. Each batch or lot number of plated or biochemical test medium should be tested. Antibiotic disks, other disks used for identification, additives for growth stimulation, and indole test reagents should be tested at weekly intervals. The following cultures should be maintained for use in quality control procedures:

B. fragilis, ATCC # 25285
B. melaninogenicus, ATCC # 25845
B. ovatus, ATCC # 8483
B. thetaiotaomicron, ATCC # 29741
B. ureolyticus
C. perfringens, ATCC # 13124
E. coli, ATCC # 25922
E. lentum
F. necrophorum
P. anaerobius
P. micros
P. mirabilis
S. faecalis, ATCC # 29212

Some of these strains are available on freeze-dried disks (Anaerobe Systems, BBL and American Type Culture Collection). Well documented laboratory strains may be used where ATCC strains are not listed.

Table A-5 Quality control procedures for media and reagents

Medium or Reagent	Test Organism	Results/Rationale
AGARS		
Blood agar	*C. perfringens*	growth, double zone of beta-hemolysis
	B. melaninogenicus	growth, pigment*
BBE	*B. fragilis*	growth, black colonies
	B. melaninogenicus	no growth, bile inhibition
	E. coli	no growth, gentamicin inhibition
KVLB	*B. melaninogenicus*	growth, black pigment*
	C. perfringens	no growth, vancomycin inhibition
	E. coli	no growth, kanamycin inhibition
PEA	*B. fragilis*	growth
	P. mirabilis	inhibition of swarming
EYA	*C. perfringens*	growth, lecithinase production
	F. necrophorum	growth, lipase production
CCFA	*C. difficile*	growth, chartreuse fluorescence
	B. fragilis	inhibition of growth by cefoxitin
	E. coli	inhibition of growth by cycloserine
DISKS		
Colistin (10 µg)	*F. necrophorum*	susceptible
	B. fragilis	resistant
Kanamycin (1 mg)	*C. perfringens*	susceptible
	B. fragilis	resistant
Vancomycin (5 µg)	*C. perfringens*	susceptible
	B. fragilis	resistant
Nitrate	*B. ureolyticus*	nitrate reduced
	B. fragilis	nitrate not reduced
SPS	*P. anaerobius*	susceptible, zone ≥12 mm
	P. micros	resistant, zone <12 mm

* pigment may require more than 48 hours incubation

Table A-5 Quality control procedures for media and reagents (cont.)

Medium or Reagent	Test Organism	Results/Rationale
GROWTH STIMULATION TESTS		
Base medium + F/F	*B. ureolyticus*	growth enhanced compared to that in base medium
Base medium + arginine	*E. lentum*	growth enhanced compared to that in base medium
Base medium + Tween 80®	*P. micros*	growth enhanced compared to that in base medium
MISCELLANEOUS		
Urea broth	*B. ureolyticus*	urease produced
	B. fragilis	urease not produced
Indole test reagents	*F. necrophorum*	indole produced
	B. fragilis	indole not produced
Thioglycolate	*B. ovatus*	growth in 24 hours
PY base	*B. ovatus*	growth in 24 hours

Table A-6 Quality control procedures for PRAS or thioglycolate-based biochemical test media.

Biochemical Test Medium	Reaction	Test Organism Growth and positive reaction	Test Organism Growth and negative reaction
Amygdalin	acid	*B. ovatus*	*P. micros*
Arabinose	acid	" "	" "
Bile	growth	" "	" "
Cellobiose	acid	" "	" "
Esculin	acid	" "	" "
	hydrolysis	" "	" "
Fructose	acid	" "	" "
Gelatin	hydrolysis	*C. perfringens*	" "
Glucose	acid	*B. ovatus*	" "
Glycerol	acid	*S. faecalis*	" "
Glycogen	acid	*B. ovatus*	" "
Lactose	acid	" "	" "
Maltose	acid	" "	" "
Mannitol	acid	*S. faecalis*	" "
Melezitose	acid	*B. ovatus*	" "
Melibiose	acid	" "	" "
Milk	clot	" "	" "
	digestion	*C. perfringens*	" "
Nitrate	reduction	*B. ureolyticus*	*B. ovatus*
Indole	production	*B. ovatus*	*B. ureolyticus*
Raffinose	acid	" "	*P. micros*
Rhamnose	acid	" "	" "
Ribose	acid	" "	" "
Salicin	acid	" "	" "
Sorbitol	acid	*S. faecalis*	" "
Starch	acid	*B. ovatus*	" "
	hydrolysis	" "	" "
Sucrose	acid	" "	" "
Trehalose	acid	" "	" "
Xylan	acid	" "	" "
Xylose	acid	" "	" "

SOURCES OF MEDIA, SUPPLIES, AND EQUIPMENT

Media and reagents

Aldrich Chemical Co., Inc.
940 West St. Paul Ave.
Milwaukee, WI 53233

Anaerobe Systems
3066 Scott Blvd.
Santa Clara, CA 95050

Analytab Products, Inc.
200 Express Street
Plainview, N.Y. 11803

Baltimore Biological
Laboratories (BBL)
Cockeysville, MD 21030

Becton-Dickinson and Co.
Rutherford, NJ 07070

Cal-Scott Laboratories
1137 Janis Street
Carson, CA 90746

Carr-Scarborough Micro-
biologicals, Inc.
P.O. Box 1328
Stone Mountain, GA 30083

Difco Laboratories
Box 1058A
Detroit, MI 48232

Eastman Organic Chemicals
Eastman Kodak Co.
Rochester, NY 14650

GIBCO
3175 Staley Rd.
Grand Island, NY 14072

Innovative Diagnostic Systems, Inc.
3404 Oakcliff Road, Ste. C-1
Atlanta, GA 30340

OXOID USA, Inc.
9017 Red Branch Rd.
Columbia, MD 21045

Remel
12076 Santa Fe Drive
P.O. Box 14428
Lenexa, KA 66215

Scott Laboratories, Inc.
Fiskeville, RI 02823

Supelco, Inc.
Supelco Park
Bellefonte, PA 16823

Wellcome Animal Health
P.O. Box 6036
Kansas City, KA 66106

Equipment and supplies

Bellco Glass, Inc.
340 Edrudo Road
Vineland, NJ 08360

Baltimore Biological Laboratories
(BBL)
Cockeysville, MD 21030

Coy Laboratory Products, Inc.
P.O. Box 1108
Ann Arbor, MI 48106

Craft Machine, Inc.
I-95 and Concord Road
Chester, PA 19013

Dodeca (formerly Capco, GLC)
P.O. Box 1383
Fremont, CA

Engelhard Industries
Gas Equipment Division
East Newark, NJ 07029

Forma Scientific
Division of Mallinckrodt, Inc.
Box 649
Mariett, OH 45750

Hewlett Packard
1820 Embarcadero Rd.
Palo Alto, CA 94303

Kontes
Spruce Street
Vineland, NJ 08360
West Coast office:
2809 Tenth Street
Berkeley, CA 94710

L & R Mfg. Co.
Kearny, NJ 07032

Marion Scientific Corp.
10236 Bunker Ridge Rd.
Kansas City, MO 64114

Micro-Media Systems, Inc.
10000 Falls Rd.
Potomac, MD 20854

Shimadzu Scientific Instruments, Inc.
7102 Riverwood Dr.
Columbia, MD 21046

Spectra-Physics
333 No. First Street
San Jose, CA 95134

Varian, Inc.
Instrument Division
611 Hansen Way
Palo Alto, CA 94303

Yamanouchi Pharmaceuticals
#5, 2-Chome, Nihon bashi-Hancho,
Chuo-ku
Tokyo, Japan

Reference cultures

American Type Culture Collection
12301 Parklawn Drive
Rockville, MD 20852

National Collection of Type Cultures
Central Public Health Laboratory
Colindale Avenue
London NW9 5HT, England

REFERENCES

1. Altemeier, W.A.: The anaerobic streptococci in tuboovarian abscess, Am. J. Obstet. Gynecol. *39*:1038-1052, 1940.
2. Altemeier, W.A.: The bacterial flora of acute perforated appendicitis with peritonitis, Ann. Surg. *107*:517-528, 1938.
3. Altemeier, W.A., and Fullen, W.D.: Prevention and treatment of gas gangrene, J.A.M.A. *217*:806-813, 1971.
4. Appelbaum, P.C., Kaufman, C.S., Keifer, J.C., and Venbrux, H.J.: Comparison of three methods for anaerobe identification, J. Clin. Microbiol. *18*:614-621, 1984.
5. Aranki, A., Syed, S.A., Kenney, E.B., and Freter, R.: Isolation of anaerobic bacteria from human gingiva and mouse cecum by means of a simplified glove box procedure, Appl. Microbiol. *17*:568-576, 1969.
6. Attebery, H.R., and Carter, W.T.: Rotator-pipette method for surface inoculation of petri plates, Abst. Ann. Meeting, Am. Soc. Microbiol., p. 11, 1972.
7. Ayyagari, A., Pancholi, V.K., Pandhi, S.C., Goswami, A., Agarwal, K.C., and Mehra, Y.N.: Anaerobic bacteria in chronic suppurative otitis media, Indian J. Med. Res. *73*:860-864, 1981.
8. Balows, A., DeHaan, R.M., Dowell, V.R., Jr., and Guze, L.B., editors: Anaerobic bacteria: role in disease, Springfield, Il., 1974, Charles C Thomas, Publisher.
9. Banno, Y., Kobayashi, T., Kono, H., Watanabe, K., Ueno, K., and Nozawa, Y.: Biochemical characterization and biologic actions of two toxins (D-1 and D-2) from *Clostridium difficile*, Rev. Infect. Dis. *6* (Suppl. 1):S11-S20, 1984.
10. Bartlett, J.G.: Laboratory diagnosis of antibiotic-associated colitis, Laboratory Medicine *12*:347-351, 1981.
11. Bartlett, J.G., and Gorbach, S.L.: Anaerobic infections of the head and neck, Otolaryngol. Clin. North Am. *9*:655-678, 1976.
12. Bartlett, J.G., Gorbach, S.L., and Finegold, S.M.: The bacteriology of aspiration pneumonia, Am. J. Med. *56*:202-207, 1974.
13. Bartlett, J.G., Gorbach, S.L., Tally, F.P., and Finegold, S.M.: Bacteriology and treatment of primary lung abscess, Am. Rev. Resp. Dis. *109*:510-518, 1974.
14. Bartlett, J.G., Gorbach, S.L., Thadepalli, H., and Finegold, S.M.: The bacteriology of empyema, Lancet *1*:338-340, 1974.
15. Bartlett, J.G., Onderdonk, A.B., Drude, E., Goldstein, C., Anderka, M., Alpert, S., McCormack, W.M.: Quantitative bacteriology of the vaginal flora, J. Infect. Dis. *136*:271-277, 1977.
16. Bartlett, J.G., and Polk, B.F.: Bacterial flora of the vagina: Quantitative study, Rev. Inf. Diseases *6*(Suppl. 1):S67-S72, 1984.
17. Bauer, A.W., Kirby, W.M.M., Sherris, J.C., and Turck, M.: Antibiotic suscepti-bility testing by a single disc method, Am. J. Clin. Pathol. *45*:493-496, 1966.
18. Beaucage, C.M., and Onderdonk, A.B.: Evaluation of prereduced anaerobically sterilized medium (PRAS II) system for identification of anaerobic microorganisms, J. Clin. Microbiol. *16*:570-572, 1982.
19. Becker, G.D., Parell, G.J., Busch, D.F., Finegold, S.M., and Acquarelli, M.J.: Anaerobic and aerobic bacteriology in head and neck cancer surgery, Arch. Otolaryn-gol. *104*:591-594, 1978.
20. Beerens, H., and Tahon-Castel, M: Infections Humaines à Bactéries Anáerobies Non Toxigènes, Bruxelles, 1965, Presses Académiques Européenes.

21. Bourgault, A-M., Rosenblatt, J.E., and Fitzgerald, R.H.: *Peptococcus magnus*: A significant human pathogen, Ann. Int, Med *93*:244-248, 1980.

22. Brook, I., Grimm, S., and Kielich, R.B.: Bacteriology of acute periapical abscess in children, J. Endodontol. *7*: 378-380, 1981.

23. Brook, I., and Finegold, S.M.: Bacteriology of chronic otitis media, J.A.M.A. *24*:487-488, 1979.

24. Buchanan, A.G.: Clinical laboratory evaluation of a reverse CAMP test for presumptive identification of *Clostridium perfringens*, J. Clin. Microbiol. *16*:761-762, 1982.

25. Buchanan, R.E., and Gibbon, N.E., editors: Bergey's Manual of Determinative Bacteriology, ed. 8, Baltimore, 1974, The Williams and Wilkins Co.

26. Cato, E.P.: Transfer of *Peptostreptococcus parvulus* (Weinberg, Nativelle, and Prévot 1937) Smith 1957 to the genus *Streptococcus: Streptococcus parvulus* (Weinberg, Nativelle, and Prévot 1937) comb. nov., nom., rev., emend. Int. J. Syst. Bacteriol. *33*:82-84, 1983.

27. Cato, E.P., Johnson, J.L., Hash, D.E., and Holdeman, L.V.: Synonomy of *Peptococcus glycinophilus* (Cardon and Barker 1946) Douglas 1957 with *Peptostreptococcus micros* (Prévot 1933) Smith 1957 and electrophoretic differentiation of *Peptostreptococcus micros* from *Peptostreptococcus magnus* (Prévot 1933) Holdeman and Moore 1972, Int. J. Syst. Bacteriol. *33*:207-210, 1983.

28. Chang, T., and Gorbach, S: Rapid identification of *Clostridium difficile* by toxin detection, J. Clin. Microbiol. *15*:465-467, 1982.

29. Chow, A.W., Galpin, J.E., and Guze, L.B.: Clinical experience with clindamycin in sepsis caused by decubitus ulcers, J. Infect. Dis. *135*:S65-S68, 1977.

30. Chow, A.W., Malkasian, K.L., Marshall, J.R., and Guze, L.B.: The bacteriology of acute pelvic inflammatory disease, Am. J. Obstet, Gynecol. *122*:876-879, 1975.

31. Chow, A.W., Roser, S.M., and Brady, F.A.: Orofacial odontogenic infections, Ann. Intern. Med. *88*:392-402, 1978.

32. Coykendall, A.L., Kaczmarek, F.S., and Slots, J.: Genetic heterogeneity in *Bacteroides asaccharolyticus* (Holdeman and Moore 1970) Finegold and Barnes 1977 (Approved Lists, 1980) and proposal of *Bacteroides gingivalis* sp. nov., and *Bacteroides macacae* (Slots and Genco) comb. nov., Int. J. Syst. Bacteriol. *30*:559-564, 1980.

33. Crawford, J.J., Sconyers, J.R., Moriarity, J.D., King, R.C., and West, J.F.: Bacteremia after tooth extraction studied with the aid of prereduced anaerobically sterilized culture media, Appl. Microbiol. *27*:927-932, 1974.

34. Dowell, V.R., Jr., and Hawkins, T.M.: Laboratory methods in anaerobic bacteriology, CDC Laboratory Manual, DHEW Publication No. (CDC) 74-8272, Washington, D.C., 1974, U.S. Government Printing Office.

35. Dowell, V.R., Jr., and Lombard, G.L.: Presumptive identification of anaerobic nonsporeforming gram-negative bacilli, Centers for Disease Control, Atlanta, GA, 1977.

36. Dowell, V.R., Jr., and Lombard, G.L.: Reactions of anaerobic bacteria in differential agar media, U.S. Department of Health and Human Services, Public Health Service, Centers for Disease Control, Atlanta, GA, 1981.

37. Dowell, V.R., Jr., Lombard, G.L., Thompson, F.S., and Armfield, A.Y.: Media for isolation, characterization, and identification of obligately anaerobic bacteria, Atlanta, GA, 1977, Centers for Disease Control

38. Draper, D.L., and Barry, A.L.: Rapid identification of *Bacteroides fragilis* with bile and antibiotic disks, J. Clin. Microbiol. *5*:439-443, 1977.

39. Edelstein, M.A.C., Citron, D.M., and Mulligan, M.E.: Preparation and storage of selective media for *Clostridium difficile,* Abst. Ann Meeting, Amer. Soc. for Microbiol., C-193, p. 344, 1983.
40. Ellen, R.P., and Balcerzak-Raczkowski, I.B.: Differential medium for detecting dental plaque bacteria resembling *Actinomyces viscosus* and *Actinomyces naeslundii,* J. Clin. Microbiol. *2*:305-310, 1975.
41. England, D.M., and Rosenblatt, J.E.: Anaerobes in human biliary tracts, J. Clin. Microbiol. *6*:494-498, 1977.
42. Ericsson, H.M., and Sherris, J.C.: Antibiotic sensitivity testing; report of an international collaborative study, 1971. Acta Pathol. Microbiol. Scand., Sect. B. Suppl. No. 217.
43. Eschenbach, D.A., Buchanan, T.M., and Pollock, H.M.: Polymicrobial etiology of acute pelvic inflammatory disease, N. Engl. J. Med. *193*:166-171, 1975.
44. Ezaki, T., Yamamoto, N., Ninomiya, K., Suzuki, S., and Yabuchi, E.: Transfer of *Peptococcus indolicus, Peptococcus asaccharolyticus, Peptococcus prevotii,* and *Peptococcus magnus* to the genus *Peptostreptococcus* and proposal of *Peptostreptococcus tetradius* sp. nov., Int. J. Syst. Bacteriol. *33*:683-698, 1983.
45. Felner, J.M., and Dowell, V.R., Jr.: "Bacteroides" bacteremia, Am. J. Med. *50*:787-796, 1971.
46. Finegold, S.M.: Anaerobic bacteria in human disease, New York, 1977, Academic Press, Inc.
47. Finegold, S.M., and Martin, W.J., Diagnostic Microbiology, 6th Ed., 1982, St. Louis, The C.V. Mosby Co.
48. Finegold, S.M., Sutter, V.L., and Mathisen, G.E.: Normal indigenous intestinal flora. Chap. 1 in Hentges, D.J. (ed), Human intestinal flora in health and disease, New York, 1983, Academic Press, Inc.
49. Finegold, S.M., Sugihara, P.T., and Sutter, V.L.: Use of selective media for isolation of anaerobes. In Shapton, D.A., and Board, R.G., (eds): Isolation of anaerobes, London, 1971, Academic Press, Inc., pp 99-108.
50. Flodstrom, A., and Hallander, H.O.: Microbiological aspects of peritonsillar abscesses, Scan. J. Infect. Dis *8*:157-160, 1976.
51. Flora, D., Wideman, P., Sutter, V.L., and Finegold, S.M.: Unpublished data.
52. Frederick, J., and Braude, A.I.: Anaerobic infection of the paranasal sinuses, N. Engl. J. Med. *290*:135-137, 1974.
53. Freier, P.A., Graves, M.H., and Kocka, F.E.: A rapid glutamic decarboxylase test for identification of bacteria, Ann. Clin. Lab. Science *6*:537-539, 1976.
54. George, W.L., Sutter, V.L., Citron, D., and Finegold, S.M.: Selective and differential medium for isolation of *C. difficile,* J. Clin. Microbiol. *9*:214-219, 1979.
55. Goldstein, E.J.C., Citron, D.M., Wield, B., Blachman, U., Sutter, V.L., Miller, T.A., and Finegold, S.M.: Bacteriology of human and animal bite wounds, J. Clin. Microbiol. *8*:667-672, 1978.
56. Gonzales-C, C.L., and Calia, F.M.: Bacteriologic flora of aspiration induced pulmonary infections, Arch. Intern. Med. *135*:711-714, 1975.
57. Goodman, A.D.: Isolation of anaerobic bacteria from the root canal systems of necrotic teeth by use of a transport solution, Oral Surg. *43*:766-770, 1977.
58. Gorbach, S.L.: Management of anaerobic infections: intra-abdominal sepsis, Ann. Intern. Med. *83*:377-379, 1975.
59. Gorbach, S.L., Mayhew, J.W., Bartlett, J.G., Thadepalli, H., and Onderdonk,

A.B., Rapid diagnosis of anaerobic infections by direct gas-liquid chromatography of clinical specimens, J. Clin. Invest. *57*:478-484, 1976.

60. Gorbach, S.L., Mayhew, J.W., Bartlett, J.G., Thadepalli, H., and Onderdonk, A.B.: Rapid diagnosis of *Bacteroides fragilis* by direct gas-liquid chromatography of clinical specimens, Clin. Res. *22*:442a, 1974.

61. Gorbach, S.L., Thadepalli, H., and Norsen, J.: Anaerobic microorganisms in intra-abdominal infections. In Balows, A., and others, editors: Anaerobic bacteria: role in disease, Springfield, Il., 1974, Charles C Thomas, Publisher, pp. 399-407.

62. Gregory, E.M.,, Veltri, B.J., Wagner, D.L., and Wilkins, T.D.: Carbohydrate repression of catalase synthesis in *Bacteroides fragilis*, J. Bacteriol. *129*:534-535, 1977.

63. Hall, W.L., Sobel, A.I., Jones, C.P., and Parker, R.T.: Anaerobic postoperative pelvic infections, Obstet. Gynecol. *30*:1-7, 1967.

64. Hamory, B.H., Sande, M.A., Sydnor, A., Jr., Seale, D.L., and Gwaltney, J.M., Jr.: Etiology and antimicrobial therapy of acute maxillary sinusitus, J. Infect. Dis. *139*:197-202, 1979.

65. Hansen, M.V., and Elliott, L.P.: New presumptive indentification test for *Clostridium perfringens*: reverse CAMP test, J. Clin. Microbiol. *12*:617-619, 1980.

66. Hansen, S., Pope, W., Weinberg, L., and Smith, L.: The value of rapid tests for identification of clinically isolated anaerobes. Abst. Ann. Meeting, Amer. Soc. Microbiol., C-26, p. 267, 1981.

67. Hauser, K.J., Johnston, J.A., and Zabransky, R.J.: An economical agar dilution technique for susceptibility testing of anaerobes, Antimicrob. Agents Chemother. *7*:712-714, 1975.

68. Heineman, H.S., and Braude, A.I.: Anaerobic infection of the brain, Am. J. Med. *35*:682-697, 1963.

68a. Helstad, A.G., Hutchinson, M.A., Amos, W.P., and Kurzynski, T.A.: Evaluation of two broth disk methods for antibiotic susceptibility of anaerobes. Antimicrob. Agents Chemother. *26*:601-603, 1984.

69. Holdeman, L.V., Cato, E.P., and Moore, W.E.C., editors: Anaerobe laboratory manual, ed. 4, Blacksburg, VA, 1977, Virginia Polytechnic Institute and State University.

70. Holdeman, L.V., Cato, E.P., and Moore, W.E.C.: Taxonomy of anaerobes: Present state of the art, Rev. Infect. Dis. *6*(Suppl. 1):S3-S10, 1984.

71. Holdeman, L.V., and Johnson, J.L.: Descriptions of *Bacteroides loescheii* sp. nov. and emendation of the descriptions of *Bacteroides melaninogenicus* (Oliver and Wherry) Roy and Kelly 1939 and *Bacteroides denticola* Shah and Collins 1981, Int. J. Syst. Bacteriol. *32*:399-409, 1982.

72. Holdeman, L.V., and Moore, W.E.C.: New genus, *Coprococcus*, twelve new species, and emended descriptions of four previously described species of bacteria from human feces, Int. J. Syst. Bacteriol. *24*:260-277, 1974.

73. Holt, J.G. (Editor-in-Chief), and Krieg, N.R. (Editor, Section I): Bergey's manual of systematic bacteriology, Ninth Edition, Subvolume 1, Baltimore, MD, 1984, The Williams and Wilkins Co.

74. Hovig, B., and Aandahl, E.H.: A selective method for isolation of *Haemophilus* in material from the respiratory tract, Acta. Path. Microbiol. Scand. *77*:676-684, 1969.

75. Hungate, R.E.: A roll tube method for cultivation of strict anaerobes. In Norris, J.R., and Ribbons, D.W., editors: Methods in microbiology, vol. 3B, New York, 1969, Academic Press, Inc., pp. 117-132.

76. Husain, M., Rajashekariah, K., Menda, K., Norsen, J., and Kallick, C: Anaerobic microbiology of soft tissue abscesses. Proc. 15th Interscience Conf. on Antimicrob. Agents Chemother., Am. Soc. Microbiol., Abstract 56, 1975.

77. Iino, Y., Takasaka, T., Hoshino, E., Kaneko, Y., Tomioka, S., and Yuasa, R.: Organic acids and anaerobic microorganisms in the contents of the cholesteatoma sac, Ann. Otol. Rhinol. Laryngol. *92*:91-96, 1983.

78. Jilly, B.J.,, Schreckenberger, P.C., and LeBeau, L.J.: Rapid glutamic acid decarboxylase test for identification of *Bacteroides* and *Clostridium* spp., J. Clin. Microbiol. *19*:592-593, 1984.

79. Johnson, J.L., and Ault, D.A.: Taxonomy of the *Bacteroides*. II. Correlation of phenotypic characteristics with deoxyribonucleic acid and homology groupings for *Bacteroides fragilis* and other saccharolytic *Bacteroides* species, Int. J. Syst. Bacteriol. *28*:257-268, 1978.

80. Johnson, J.L., and Holdeman, L.V.: *Bacteroides intermedius* comb. nov. and descriptions of *Bacteroides corporis* sp. nov. and *Bacteroides levii* sp. nov., Int. J. Syst. Bacteriol. *33*:15-25, 1983.

81. Jokipii, A.M.M., Karma, P., Ojala, K., and Jokipii, L.: Anaerobic bacteria in chronic otitis media, Arch. Otolaryngol. *103*:278-280, 1977.

82. Jones, D.B., and Robinson, N.M.: Anaerobic ocular infections, Trans. Am. Acad. Ophth. & Oto. *83*:309-331, 1977.

83. Jones, R.N., Barry, A.L., Cotton, J.L., Sutter, V.L., and Swenson, J.M.: Collaborative evaluation of the Micro-Media Systems Anaerobe Susceptibility Panel: Comparisons with reference methods and test reproducibility, J. Clin. Microbiol. *16*:245-249, 1982.

84. Kaczmarek, F.S., and Coykendall, A.L.: Production of phenylacetic acid by strains of *Bacteroides asaccharolyticus* and *Bacteroides gingivalis* (sp. nov.), J. Clin. Microbiol. *12*:288-290, 1980.

85. Kilian, M., and Schiott, C.R.: Haemophili and related bacteria in the human oral cavity, Arch. Oral Biol. *20*:791-796, 1975.

86. Killgore, G.E., Starr, S.E., DelBene, V.E., Whaley, D.N., and Dowell, V.R., Jr.: Comparison of three anaerobic systems for isolation of anaerobic bacteria from clinical specimens, Am. J. Clin. Pathol. *59*:552-559, 1973.

87. Kodaka, H., Armfield, A.Y., Lombard, G.L., and Dowell, V.R., Jr.: Practical procedure for demonstrating bacterial flagella, J. Clin. Microbiol. *16*:948-952, 1982.

88. Koransky, J.R., Allen, S.D., and Dowell, V.R., Jr.: Use of ethanol for selective isolation of sporeforming microorganisms, Appl. Environ. Microbiol. *35*:762-765, 1978.

89. Kornman, K.S., and Loesche, W.J.: A new medium for isolation of *Actinomyces viscosus* and *Actinomyces naeslundii* from dental plaque, J. Clin. Microbiol. *7*: 514-518, 1978.

90. Kurzynski, T.A., Yrios, J.W., Helstad, A.G., and Field, C.R.: Aerobically incubated thioglycolate broth disk method for antibiotic susceptibility testing of anaerobes, Antimicrob. Agents Chemother. *10*:727-732, 1976.

91. Laughon, B.E., Viscidi, R.P., Gdovin, S.L., Yolken, R.H., and Bartlett, J.G.: Enzyme immunoassays for detection of *Clostridium difficile* toxins A and B in fecal specimens, J. Infect. Dis. *149*:781-788, 1984.

92. Ledger, W.J., Gee, C.L., Pollin, P., Nakamura, R.M., and Lewis, W.P.: The use of prereduced media and a portable jar for the collection of anaerobic organisms from clinical sites of infection, Am. J. Obstet. Gynecol. *125*:677-681, 1976.

93. Lenette, E.H., Balows, A., Hausler, W.J., and Shadomy, H.J., editors: Manual of clinical microbiology, ed. 4, Washington, D.C., 1985, American Society for Microbiology.

94. Levison, M.E., Trestman, I., Quach, R., Sladowski, C., and Floro, C.N.: Quantitative bacteriology of the vaginal flora in vaginitis, Am. J. Obstet. Gynecol. *133*:139-144, 1979.

95. Lewis, R.P., Sutter, V.L., and Finegold, S.M.: Bone infections involving anaerobic bacteria, Medicine *57*:279-305, 1978.

96. Livingston, S.J., Kominos, S.D., and Yee, R.B.: New medium for selection and presumptive identification of the *Bacteroides fragilis* group, J. Clin. Microbiol. *7*:448-453, 1978.

97. Loesche, W.J.: Dental infections. In Balows, A., and others, editors: Anaerobic bacteria: role in disease, Springfield, IL, 1974, Charles C Thomas, Publisher, pp. 409-434.

98. Lombard, G.L., Whaley, D.N., Dowell, V.R., Jr.: Comparison of media in the Anaerobe-Tek and Presumpto plate systems and evaluation of the Anaerobe-Tek system for identification of commonly encountered anaerobes, J. Clin. Microbiol. *16*:1066-1072, 1982.

99. Lorber, B., and Swenson, R.M.: Bacteriology of aspiration pneumonia; a prospective study of community and hospital acquired cases, Ann. Intern. Med. *81*:329-331, 1974.

100. Louie, T.J., Bartlett, J.G., Tally, F.P., and Gorbach, S.L.: Aerobic and anaerobic bacteria in diabetic foot ulcers, Ann. Intern. Med. *85*: 461-463, 1976.

101. Lyerly, D.M., Sullivan, N.M., and Wilkins, T.D.: Enzyme-linked immunosorbent assay for *Clostridium difficile* toxin A, J. Clin. Microbiol. *17*:72-78, 1983.

102. MacLennan, J.D.: The histotoxic clostridial infections of man, Bacteriol. Rev. *26*:177-276, 1962.

103. Manganiello, A.D., Socransky, S.S., Smith, C., Propas, D., Oram, V., and Dogon, I.L.: Attempts to increase viable count recovery of human supragingival dental plaque, J. Periodontal Res. *12*:107-119, 1977.

104. Marler, L.M., O'Bryan, N.B., Siders, J.A., and Allen, S.D.: Evaluation of the IDS RapID ANA system for identification of clinical anaerobic isolates, Abst. Ann. Meeting, Amer. Soc. for Microbiol., C-149, p. 261, 1984.

105. Mayrand, D.: Identification of clinical isolates of selected species of *Bacteroides*: production of phenylacetic acid, Can. J. Microbiol. *25*:927-928, 1979.

106. Mayrand, D., and Bourgeau, G.: Production of phenylacetic acid by anaerobes, J. Clin. Microbiol. *16*:747-750, 1982.

107. Mays, T.D., Holdeman, L.V., Moore, W.E.C., Rogosa, M., and Johnson, J.L.: Taxonomy of the genus *Veillonella* Prévot, Int. J. Syst. Bacteriol. *32*:28-36, 1982.

108. Meislin, H.W., Lerner, S.A., Graves, M.H., McGehee, M.D., Kocka, F.E., Morello, J.A., and Rosen, P.: Cutaneous abscesses. Anaerobic and aerobic bacteriology and outpatient management, Ann. Intern. Med. *87*:145-149, 1977.

109. Mitruka, B.M.: Presumptive diagnosis of infectious diseases. In Mitruka, B.M., editor: Gas chromatographic applications in microbiology and medicine, New York, 1975, John Wiley & Sons, Inc., pp. 349-374.

110. Mitsuoka, T., Ohno, K., Benno, Y., Suzuki, K., and Namba, K.: The fecal flora of man. IV Communication: Comparison of the newly developed method with the old conventional method for analysis of intestinal flora, Zbl. Bakt. Hyg., Abt. Orig. A234:219-233, 1976.

111. Moore, W.E.C., Cato, E.P., and Holdeman, L.V.: Anaerobic bacteria of the gastrointestinal flora and their occurrence in clinical infections, J. Infect. Dis. *119*:641-649, 1969.

112. Morgenstein, A.A., Citron, D.M., and Finegold, S.M.: New medium selective for *Fusobacterium* species and differential for *Fusobacterium necrophorum*, J. Clin. Microbiol. *13*:666-669, 1981.

113. Mouton, C., Hammond, P., Slots, J., and Genco, R.J.: Evaluation of Fluoretec-M for detection of oral strains of *Bacteroides asaccharolyticus* and *Bacteroides melaninogenicus*, J. Clin. Microbiol. *11*:682-686, 1980.

114. Mulligan, M.E., Citron, D.M., McNamara, B.T., and Finegold, S.M.: Impact of cefoperazone therapy on fecal flora, Antimicrob. Agents Chemother. *22*:226-230, 1982.

115. Murray, P.R., and Niles, A.C.: Inoculum preparation for anaerobic susceptibility tests, J. Clin. Microbiol. *18*:733-734, 1983.

116. Murray, P.R., and Niles, A.C.: Modified method of preparing inoculum for anaerobic susceptibility tests. Abst. #394 Interscience Conference on Antimicrobial Agents and Chemotherapy, 1982.

117. Murray, P.R., and Sondag, J.E.: Evaluation of routine subcultures of macroscopically negative blood cultures for detection of anaerobes, J. Clin. Microbiol. *8*:427-430, 1978.

118. National Committee for Clinical Laboratory Standards: Standard procedures for handling and transport of diagnostic medical specimens and etiologic agents, TSH-5, NCCLS, Villanova, PA, 1978, The Committee.

119. National Committee for Clinical Laboratory Standards. 1985. Approved standard reference agar dilution procedure for antimicrobial susceptibility testing of anaerobic bacteria, Vol. 5, pp. 25-38. National Committee for Clinical Laboratory Standards, Villanova, PA.

120. Newman, M.G., and Sims, T.N.: The predominant cultivable microbiota of the periodontal abscess, J. Periodontol. *50*:350-354, 1979.

121. Olsen, I., and Socransky, S.S.: Comparison of three anaerobic culture techniques and media for viable recovery of subgingival plaque bacteria, Scand. J. Dent. Res. *89*:165-174, 1981.

122. Paisley, J.W., Rosenblatt, J.E., Hall, M., and Washington, J.A. II: Evaluation of a routine anaerobic subculture of blood cultures for detection of anaerobic bacteremia, J. Clin. Microbiol. *8*:764-766, 1978.

123. Parker, R.T., and Jones, C.P.: Anaerobic pelvic infections and developments in hyperbaric oxygen therapy, Am. J. Obstet. Gynecol. *96*:645-658, 1966.

124. Pearson, H.E., and Smiley, D.F.: Bacteroides in pilonidal sinuses, Am. J. Surg. *115*:336-338, 1968.

125. Perry, L.D., Brinser, J.H., and Kolodner, H.: Anaerobic corneal ulcers, Ophthalmol. *89*:636-642, 1982.

126. Pheifer, T.A., Forsyth, P.S., Durfee, M.A., Pollock, H.M., Holmes, K.K.: Nonspecific vaginitis, New Engl. J. Med. *298*:1429-1434, 1978.

127. Phillips, K.D., and Rogers, P.A.: Rapid detection and presumptive identification of *Clostridium difficile* by *p*-cresol production on a selective medium, J. Clin. Pathol. *34*:642-644, 1981.

128. Phillips, K.D., Tearle, P.J., and Willis, A.T.: Rapid diagnosis of anaerobic infections by gas-liquid chromatography of clinical materials, J. Clin. Pathol. *29*:428-432, 1976.

129. Poxton, I.R., and Byrne, M.D.: Detection of *Clostridium difficile* toxin by counterimmunoelectrophoresis: a note of caution, J. Clin. Microbiol. *14*:349, 1981.

130. Qadri, S.M.H., Johnson, S., Smith, J.C., Zubairi, S., and Gillum, R.L.: Comparison of spot esculin hydrolysis with the PathoTec strip test for rapid differentiation of anaerobic bacteria, J. Clin. Microbiol. *13*:459-462, 1981.

131. Ristow, K.L., Schreckenberger, P.C., Celig, D.M., Ulanday, M.A., and Le Beau, L.J.: Evaluation of the RapID ANA system for identification of anaerobic bacteria from clinical specimens, Abst. Ann. Meeting, Amer. Soc. for Microbiol., C-151, p. 261, 1984.

132. Rolfe, R.D., and Finegold, S.M.: Purification and characterization of *Clostridium difficile* toxin, Infection and Immunity *25*:191-201, 1979.

133. Rosebury, T.: Microorganisms indigenous to man, New York, 1962, McGraw-Hill Book Co.

134. Rosenblatt, J.E., Fallon, A.M., and Finegold, S.M.: Comparison of methods for isolation of anaerobic bacteria from clinical specimens, Appl. Microbiol. *25*:77-85, 1973.

135. Rotheram, E.B., Jr., and Schick, S.F.: Non-clostridial anaerobic bacteria in septic abortion, Am. J. Med. *46*:80-89, 1969.

136. Sabbaj, J., Sutter, V.L., and Finegold, S.M.: Anaerobic pyogenic liver abscess, Ann. Intern. Med. *77*:629-638, 1972.

137. Salyers, A.A., Vercellotti, J.R., West, S.E.H., and Wilkins, T.D.: Fermentation of mucin and plant polysaccharides by strains of *Bacteroides* from the human colon, Appl. Environ. Microbiol. *33*:319-322, 1977.

138. Sapico, F.L., Canawati, H.N., Witte, J.L., Montgomerie, J.Z., Wagner, F.W., Jr., and Bessman, A.N.: Quantitative aerobic and anaerobic bacteriology of infected diabetic feet, J. Clin. Microbiol. *12*:413-420, 1980.

139. Schwan, O.: Biochemical, enzymatic, and serological differentiation of *Peptococcus indolicus* (Christiansen) Sorensen from *Peptococcus asaccharolyticus* (Distaso) Douglas, J. Clin. Microbiol. *9*:157-162, 1979.

140. Shanholtzer, C.J., Peterson, L.R., Olson, M.N., and Gerding, D.N.: Prospective study of gram-stained stool smears in diagnosis of *Clostridium difficile* colitis, J. Clin. Microbiol. *17*:906-908, 1983.

141. Shimada, K., Inamatsu, T., and Yamashiro, M.: Anaerobic bacteria in biliary disease in elderly patients, J. Infect. Dis. *135*:850-854, 1977.

142. Slots, J., and Genco, R.J.: *Bacteroides melaninogenicus* subsp. *macacae*, a new subspecies from monkey periodontopathic indigenous microflora, Int. J. Syst. Bacteriol. *30*:82-85, 1980.

143. Slots, J., Potts, T.V., and Mashimo, P.A.: *Fusobacterium periodonticum*, a new species from the human oral cavity, J. Dent. Res. *62*:960-963, 1983.

144. Slots, J., and Reynolds, H.S.: Longwave UV light fluorescence for identification of black-pigmented *Bacteroides* spp., J. Clin. Microbiol. *16*:1148-1151, 1982.

145. Smith, J.W., Southern, P.M., Jr., and Lehmann, J.D.: Bacteremia in septic abortion; complications and treatment, Obstet. Gynecol. *35*: 704-708, 1970.

146. Smith, R.F., Rogers, R.R., and Bettge, C.L.: Inhibition of the indole test reaction by sodium nitrite, Appl. Microbiol. *23*:423-424, 1972.

147. Sondag, J.E., Ali, M., and Murray, P.R.: Relative recovery of anaerobes on different isolation media, J. Clin. Microbiol. *10*:756-757, 1979.

148. Sondag, J.E., Ali, M., and Murray, P.R.: Rapid presumptive identification of anaerobes in blood cultures by gas-liquid chromatography, J. Clin. Microbiol. *11*:274-277, 1980.

149. Sperry, J.F., Appleman, M.D., and Wilkins, T.D.: Requirement of heme for growth of *Bacteroides fragilis*, Appl. Environ. Microbiol. *34*: 386-390, 1977.

150. Spiegel, C.A., Amsel, R., Eschenbach, D., Schoenknecht, F.D., and Holmes, K.: Anaerobic bacteria in non-specific vaginitis, N. Engl. J. Med. *303*:601-607, 1980.

151. Spiegel, C.A., Eschenbach, D.A., Amsel, R., and Holmes, K.K.: Curved anaerobic bacteria in bacterial (non-specific) vaginosis and their response to antimicrobial therapy, J. Infect. Dis. *148*:817-822, 1983.

152. Spiegel, C.A., and Roberts, M: *Mobiluncus* gen nov., *Mobiluncus curtisii* subsp. *curtisii* sp. nov. *Mobiluncus curtisii* subsp. *holmesii* subsp. nov., and *Mobiluncus mulieris* sp. nov., curved rods from the human vagina, Int. J. Syst. Bacteriol. *34*:177-184, 1984.

153. Stalons, D.R., and Thornsberry, C.: Broth-dilution methods for determining the antibiotic susceptibility of anaerobic bacteria, Antimicrob. Agents Chemother. *7*:15-21, 1975.

154. Steers, E., Foltz, E.L., and Graves, B.S.: An inocula-replicating apparatus for routine testing of bacterial susceptibility to antibiotics, Antibiot. Chemother. *9*:307-311, 1959.

155. Sundqvist, G.K.: Bacteriologic studies of necrotic dental pulps, Odontological Dissertation No. 7, University of Umea, Umea, Sweden, 1976.

156. Sutter, V.L.: Anaerobes as normal oral flora, Rev. Inf. Diseases *6* (Suppl. 1):S62-S66, 1984.

157. Sutter, V.L., Barry, A.L., Wilkins, T.D., and Zabransky, R.J.: Collaborative evaluation of a proposed reference dilution method of susceptibility testing of anaerobic bacteria, Antimicrob. Ag. Chemother. *16*:495-502, 1979.

158. Sutter, V.L., and Carter, W.T.: Evaluation of media and reagents for indole-spot tests in anaerobic bacteriology, Am. J. Clin. Pathol. *58*:335-338, 1972.

159. Sutter, V.L., and Finegold, S.M.: Antibiotic susceptibility tests for rapid presumptive identification of gram-negative anaerobic bacilli, Appl. Microbiol. *21*:13-20, 1971.

160. Sutter, V.L., Sugihara, P.T., and Finegold, S.M.: Rifampin blood agar as a selective medium for the isolation of certain anaerobic bacteria, Appl. Microbiol. *22*:777-780, 1971.

161. Swartz, M.N., and Karchmer, A.W.: Infections of the central nervous system. In Balows, A., and others, eds: Anaerobic bacteria: role in disease, Springfield, IL. 1974, Charles C Thomas, Publisher, pp. 309-325.

162. Swensen, J.M., and Thornsberry, C.: Preparing inoculum for susceptibility testing of anaerobes, J. Clin. Microbiol. *19*:321-325, 1984.

163. Swenson, R.M., Lorber, B., Michaelson, T.C., and Spaulding, E.H.: The bacteriology of intra-abdominal infections, Arch. Surg. *109*:398-399, 1974.

164. Swenson, R.M., Michaelson, T.C., Daly, M.J., and Spaulding, E.H.: Anaerobic bacterial infections of the female genital tract, Obstet. Gynecol. *42*:538-541, 1973.

165. Syed, S.A., and Loesche, W.J.: Efficiency of various growth media in recovering oral bacterial flora from human dental plaque, Appl. Microbiol. *26*:459-465, 1973.

166. Tanner, A.C.R., Badger, S., Lai, C-H., Listgarten, M.A., Visconti, R.A., and Socransky, S.S.: *Wolinella* gen. nov., *Wolinella succinogenes (Vibrio succinogenes* Wolin et al.) comb. nov., and description of *Bacteroides gracilis* sp. nov., *Wolinella recta* sp. nov., *Campylobacter concisus* sp. nov., and *Eikenella corrodens* from humans with periodontal disease, Int. J. Syst. Bacteriol. *31*:432-445, 1981.

167. Thadepalli, H., Gorbach, S.L., and Keith, L.: Anaerobic infections of the female genital tract — bacteriologic and therapeutic aspects, Am. J. Obstet. Gynecol. *117*:1034-1040, 1973.

168. Totten, P.A., Amsel, R., Hale, J., Piot, P., and Holmes, K.K.: Selective differential human blood bilayer media for isolation of *Gardnerella vaginalis*, J. Clin. Microbiol. *15*:141-147, 1982.

169. Van Steenbergen, T.J.M, Van Winkelhoff, A.J., Mayrand, D., Grenier, D., and De Graff, J.: *Bacteroides endodontalis* sp. nov., an asaccharolytic black-pigmented *Bacteroides* species from infected dental root canals, Int. J. Syst. Bacteriol. *34*:118-120, 1984.

170. Van Steenbergen, T.J.M., Vlaanderen, C.A., and De Graaff, J.: Confirmation of *Bacteroides gingivalis* as a species distinct from *Bacteroides asaccharolyticus*, Int. J. Syst. Bacteriol. *31*:236-241, 1981.

171. Walker, C.B., Ratliff, D., Muller, D., Mandell, R., and Socransky, S.S.: Medium for selective isolation of *Fusobacterium nucleatum* from human periodontal pockets, J. Clin. Microbiol. *10*:844-849, 1979.

172. Washington, J.A. II: Anaerobic blood cultures. In Lennette, E.H., Spaulding, E.H., and Truant, J.P., editors: Manual of clinical microbiology, ed. 2, Washington, D.C., 1974, American Society for Microbiology, pp. 402-404.

173. Watabe, J., Benno, Y., and Mitsuoka, T.: Taxonomic study of *Bacteroides oralis* and related organisms and proposal of *Bacteroides veroralis* sp. nov., Int. J. Syst. Bacteriol. *33*:57-64, 1983.

174. Weinberg, L.G., Smith, L.L., and McTighe, A.H.: Rapid identification of the *Bacteroides fragilis* group by bile disk and catalase tests, Laboratory Medicine *14*:785-788, 1983.

175. Weissfeld, A.S., and Sonnenwirth, A.C.: Rapid detection and identification of *Bacteroides fragilis* and *Bacteroides melaninogenicus* by immunofluorescence, J. Clin. Microbiol. *13*:798-800, 1981.

176. Welch, O.F., Menge, S.K., and Matsen, J.M.: Identification of toxigenic *C. difficile* by counterimmunoelectrophoresis, J. Clin. Microbiol. *11*:470-473, 1980.

177. West, S.E.H., and Wilkins, T.D.: Problems associated with counter immunoelectrophoresis assays for detecting *Clostridium difficile* toxin, J. Clin. Microbiol. *15*:347-349, 1982.

178. Wideman, P.A., Citronbaum, D.M., and Sutter, V.L.: Simple disk test for detection of nitrate reduction by anaerobic bacteria, J. Clin. Microbiol. *5*:315-319, 1977.

179. Wideman, P.A., Vargo, V.L., Citronbaum, D., and Finegold, S.M.: Evaluation of the sodium polyanethol sulfonate disk test for the identification of *Peptostreptococcus anaerobius*, J. Clin. Microbiol. *4*:330-333, 1976.

180. Wilkins, T.D., and Chalgren, S.: Medium for use in antibiotic susceptibility testing of anaerobic bacteria, Antimicrob. Agents Chemother. *10*:926-928, 1976.

181. Wilkins, T.D., Wagner, D.L., Veltri, B.J., Jr., and Gregory, E.M.: Factors affecting production of catalase by *Bacteroides*, J. Clin. Microbiol. *8*:553-557, 1978.

182. Williams, B.L., McCann, G.F., and Schoenknecht, F.D.: Bacteriology of dental abscesses of endodontic origin, J. Clin. Microbiol. *18*:770-774, 1983.

183. Wimberley, N., Faling, L.J., and Bartlett, J.G.: A fiberoptic bronchoscopy technique to obtain uncontaminated lower airway secretions for bacterial culture, Am. Rev. Resp. Dis. *119*:337-343, 1979.

184. Zabransky, R., Birk, R., Helstad, A., Murray, P., Emmerman, J., and Sutter, V. Establishment of MIC values of a variety of antibiotics for the NCCLS control and reference strains for antibiotic testing of anaerobic bacteria, Abstract #168, Interscience Conference on Antimicrobial Agents and Chemotherapy, 1983.

185. Zabransky, R.J., Randall, E., Sutter, V.L., Birk, R.J., Westenfelder, G., Emmerman, J., and Ghoneim, A.T.M.: Establishment of minimum inhibitory concentrations of cefoperazone for control and reference anaerobic organisms, J. Clin. Microbiol. *17*:711-714, 1983.

186. Zylber, L.J., and Jordan, H.V.: Development of a selective medium for detection and enumeration of *Actinomyces viscosus* and *Actinomyces naeslundii* in dental plaque, J. Clin. Microbiol. *15*:253-259, 1982.

INDEX